CHALLEN

❖

NUMBER FOUR

Junior Problems

based on the
Junior Mathematical Challenge
1997–2016

Andrew Jobbings

**United Kingdom
Mathematics Trust**

Junior Problems

Published by The United Kingdom Mathematics Trust.

Maths Challenges Office, School of Mathematics, University of Leeds, Leeds LS2 9JT, United Kingdom

https://www.ukmt.org.uk

First published 2017.

Reprinted 2019.

ISBN 978-1-906001-30-8

Printed in the UK for the UKMT by The Charlesworth Press, Wakefield.

http://www.charlesworth.com

Typographic design by Andrew Jobbings of Arbelos.

http://www.arbelos.co.uk

Typeset with LaTeX.

The books published by the United Kingdom Mathematics Trust are grouped into series.

The EXCURSIONS IN MATHEMATICS series consists of monographs which focus on a particular topic of interest and investigate it in some detail, using a wide range of ideas and techniques. They are aimed at high school students, undergraduates and others who are prepared to pursue a subject in some depth, but do not require specialised knowledge.

1. *The Backbone of Pascal's Triangle*, Martin Griffiths

2. *A Prime Puzzle*, Martin Griffiths

The HANDBOOKS series is aimed particularly at students at secondary school who are interested in acquiring the knowledge and skills which are useful for tackling challenging problems, such as those posed in the competitions administered by the UKMT and similar organisations.

1. *Plane Euclidean Geometry: Theory and Problems*, A D Gardiner and C J Bradley

2. *Introduction to Inequalities*, C J Bradley

3. *A Mathematical Olympiad Primer*, Geoff C Smith

4. *Introduction to Number Theory*, C J Bradley

5. *A Problem Solver's Handbook*, Andrew Jobbings

6. *Introduction to Combinatorics*, Gerry Leversha and Dominic Rowland

7. *First Steps for Problem Solvers*, Mary Teresa Fyfe and Andrew Jobbings

8. *A Mathematical Olympiad Companion*, Geoff C Smith

The PATHWAYS series aims to provide classroom teaching material for use in secondary schools. Each title develops a subject in more depth and in more detail than is normally required by public examinations or national curricula.

1. *Crossing the Bridge*, Gerry Leversha

2. *The Geometry of the Triangle*, Gerry Leversha

❖

The PROBLEMS series consists of collections of high-quality and original problems of Olympiad standard.

1. *New Problems in Euclidean Geometry*, David Monk

The CHALLENGES series is aimed at students at secondary school who are interested in tackling stimulating problems, such as those posed in the Mathematical Challenges administered by the UKMT and similar organisations.

1. *Ten Years of Mathematical Challenges: 1997 to 2006*

2. *Ten Further Years of Mathematical Challenges: 2006 to 2016*

3. *Intermediate Problems*, Andrew Jobbings

4. *Junior Problems*, Andrew Jobbings

5. *Senior Problems*, Andrew Jobbings

❖

The YEARBOOKS series documents all the UKMT activities, including details of all the challenge papers and solutions, lists of high scorers, accounts of the IMO and Olympiad training camps, and other information about the Trust's work during each year.

Contents

II More challenging problems

Miscellany 4 **139**

III Remarks and answers

Appendix

Series Editor's Foreword

This book is part of a series whose aim is to help young mathematicians prepare for competitions at secondary school level. Here the focus is on the questions from the Junior Mathematical Challenge papers. Like other volumes in the Challenges series, it provides cheap and ready access to directly relevant material.

I hope that every secondary school will have these books in its library. The prices have been set so low that many good students will wish to purchase their own copies. Schools wishing to give out large numbers of copies of these books, perhaps as prizes, should note that discounts may be negotiated with the UKMT office.

London, UK   GERRY LEVERSHA

About the Author

Andrew Jobbings gained both his BSc and his PhD in mathematics from Durham University. He taught mathematics for 28 years, including 14 years as Head of Department at Bradford Grammar School, before founding the publishing business Arbelos.

With a keen interest in providing mathematics enrichment activities, Andrew devises problems for the UKMT and is involved with many other UKMT projects. He has regularly chaired a problems group for the European Kangaroo contest and gives Royal Institution masterclasses.

Preface

The Junior Mathematical Challenge (JMC) began in 1997, after the UKMT was founded. Prior to that, equivalent challenges were organised by Tony Gardiner, under the aegis of *The UK Mathematics Foundation*.

The problems on the JMC papers are intended to be stimulating as well as challenging—ideally, some problems will raise a smile. That these aims are so admirably fulfilled is a measure of the quality of the problem setters.

Acknowledgements

Many people have been involved in the JMC since it began, including problem setters, checkers, and teachers in schools. Howard Groves has done sterling work over many years as Chair of the Problems Group. All of them, especially Tony Gardiner and Howard, deserve thanks for their help and support over the years of the competition.

I should particularly like to thank the following, who commented extremely helpfully on one or more draft versions of the book: Mary Teresa Fyfe; Calum Kilgour; Howard Groves; Stephen Power; Alan Slomson. There is no doubt that the book has improved immeasurably as a result.

Of course, any remaining mistakes are entirely the responsibility of the author.

Baildon, Shipley, UK   ANDREW JOBBINGS

Introduction

Solving a problem for which you know
there's an answer is like climbing a
mountain with a guide, along a trail
someone else has laid. In mathematics,
the truth is somewhere out there in a
place no one knows, beyond all the
beaten paths. And it's not always at the
top of the mountain. It might be in a
crack on the smoothest cliff or
somewhere deep in the valley.

Yōko Ogawa
The Housekeeper and the Professor

Layout of the book

The Junior Mathematical Challenge (JMC) is a multiple-choice competition
with 25 questions.

Problems

This book includes every problem used in the JMC from 1997 to 2016, but
these are not given as multiple-choice questions. In most cases the five
options have just been removed, but in a few cases, such as question 1 of
exercise 1, the problem has been reworded to accommodate the options.
In addition, the wording of some problems has been mildly edited.

The problems have been grouped together in two ways: by difficulty;
and by topic.

Part I consists of problems appearing earlier on in the JMC papers (up to question 15); these are intended to be more straightforward than the later problems, which are given in part II.

In each of parts I and II, problems broadly based on the same topic have been grouped together into one exercise. In each exercise, the questions are ordered by their position on the original paper. The exercises themselves are roughly ordered by difficulty.

The allocation of problems to topic areas involves a great deal of subjectivity—and is sometimes a little arbitrary—so do not be surprised if you find a problem in an unusual place. Also, the names of the topics may bear little resemblance to anything you have already met; even when you have come across a topic before, the content could well be different to anything you may be used to. The real reason for grouping the problems, of course, is that it is convenient for the author to do so!

To help indicate the degree of difficulty of each question, the number of the question on the original paper is written in the left margin. This is a rough guide only, because the Problem Group's view of the difficulty of a question can be out of line with the outcome. In any case, removing the multiple-choice options may well affect the difficulty.

Remarks

Part III consists of remarks and answers.

Nearly every problem has a remark of some sort. In some cases the results needed for the given method are listed at the start of a remark, using the symbol '☞' to indicate each result.

The remarks are not intended to be 'full written solutions' (so would not get many marks in an Olympiad-style competition), but instead sketch out one method, providing a sequence of pointers so that, hopefully, by reading them you can solve a problem yourself. Sometimes a remark is just a collection of signposts and filling in the gaps may not be straightforward. Several of the remarks refer to non-standard methods.

Though it is not necessary if you are using this book, you may wish to read fuller solutions. These are provided by the UKMT in the solutions booklets, the Yearbooks, and (more recently) the extended solutions.

Note that the methods referred to in the remarks are not based on those given elsewhere: they may be the same; sometimes they are completely different.

Answers

The answer to every problem in the book is given in part III. The answers are upside down, to help you avoid reading them inadvertently.

Of course, the answer to a problem is unimportant in itself, other than as a (potential) check on the validity of the method used. What really matters is that you understand the underlying mathematics.

Using the book

The whole purpose of this book is to provide you with problems to solve. Removing the multiple-choice element means that you actually do need to solve the mathematical problem, rather than use other techniques (such as knowing that exactly one of the options is correct).

Select a problem and have a go. Use pencil and paper to do some calculations, or draw some diagrams, whatever is necessary to make a determined effort to solve the problem. In that way you will properly engage with the problem, and the mathematics contained in it. Do this *before* looking at part III. There are three possible outcomes.

✳ You do the problem and get it right.

Well done! Even in this case it is worth reading any remarks: if your approach is the same as the one given, then you can confirm that your method is correct, otherwise, you may well learn something useful!

✳ You do the problem, but get it wrong.

After checking that you have read the question correctly, see if knowing the correct answer enables you to find an error, either in your working or your approach. Otherwise, read any remarks and try again.

✳ You cannot do the problem.

See if knowing the correct answer helps you to get there. Otherwise, read any remarks and try again. If you still have no joy, then ask someone.

You may find, partway through reading a remark, that you think 'Aha, gotcha, now I see how to do it!'. Then so much the better: stop reading and tackle the problem again. Conversely, you may find a remark too obscure. This is not deliberate (though the remarks are intended to leave you with some work to do). If you do find that you do not understand a remark and still cannot do a problem, try again later, or ask someone else.

As mentioned above, some remarks give a list of useful results. You may not yet have come across all of these; at the very least, try to find out why a result is true, either by proving it yourself, or perhaps by asking someone.

Often there is more than one way to tackle a problem, so your ideas may well differ from the method used in part III. This does not mean that your ideas are not valid—far from it—but it may be worth trying to remember the alternative approach because this could be useful in similar problems. Indeed, one measure of the quality of a problem is the number of different approaches that are possible.

Wait until you are ready before you tackle the harder problems; this applies particularly to the problems in part II.

When faced with unusual or challenging problems, what you need above all is perseverance, the desire to keep trying until some progress is made. Take your time when trying such a problem and keep puzzling away until it yields up its secrets. Success is rarely a question of extra knowledge, more often one of know-how.

In the JMC itself, of course, you are working against the clock. In such circumstances, having the relevant knowledge and know-how at your fingertips—being *fluent* in mathematics—is bound to be helpful. And that is where practice comes in, which brings us back to the purpose of this book.

Finally, suppose that you want to find a particular problem, one that you recall involves 'turnips', say. In that case you should try the index.

Calculators

Calculators are not allowed in the JMC.

In many of these problems a calculator offers no advantage, but many of the more arithmetical questions lose their point if you use a calculator.

You are advised not to use a calculator for any of the problems in the book.

Notation and terminology

You may occasionally find that the book uses notation or terminology which is not familiar to you, such as *km/h* for kilometres per hour, or *average* for what is sometimes called the mean.

Should you have any doubt about notation or terminology, please ask someone.

Part I

Problems

Arithmetic

Exercise 1

1. Which of the following five calculations gives an answer that is closer to zero than the other four?

$$6+5+4 \qquad 6+5-4 \qquad 6+5\times 4 \qquad 6-5\times 4 \qquad 6\times 5\div 4$$

2. Which of the following five calculations gives the largest answer?

$$1-2+3+4 \qquad 1+2-3+4 \qquad 1+2+3-4 \qquad 1+2-3-4$$
$$1-2-3+4$$

3. What is the value of $(999 - 99 + 9) \div 9$?

4. Which of the following five expressions gives the largest answer?

$$1-0.1 \qquad 1-0.01 \qquad 1-0.001 \qquad 1-0.0001 \qquad 1-0.00001$$

5. What is the value of $2 \times 0 \times 1 + 1$?

6. What is the value of $2010 + (+2010) + (-2010) - (+2010) - (-2010)$?

7. What is the value of $9002 - 2009$?

8. What is the value of $0.1 + 0.2 + 0.3 \times 0.4$?

1 **9.** What is the value of $6002 - 2006$?

1 **10.** What is the value of $1000 - 100 + 10 - 1$?

1 **11.** What is half of 199?

1 **12.** What is the value of 2002×5?

1 **13.** What is half of 999?

1 **14.** Four lamp-posts are in a straight line. The distance from each post to the next is 25 m.

   What is the distance from the first post to the last?

2 **15.** What number is twenty-one less than sixty thousand?

2 **16.** What is half of 1.01?

2 **17.** Which of the following five statements is false?

$$3 + 5 \times 4 = 23 \qquad 20 - 5 \times 4 = 0 \qquad 12 - 5 \times 2 = 2$$
$$3 + 6 \times 4 = 36 \qquad 5 \times 3 - 2 = 13$$

3 **18.** One lap of a standard running track is 400 m.

   How many laps does each athlete run in a 5000 m race?

3 **19.** Which of the following five statements is correct?

$$0 \times 9 + 9 \times 0 = 9 \qquad 1 \times 8 + 8 \times 1 = 18 \qquad 2 \times 7 + 7 \times 2 = 27$$
$$3 \times 6 + 6 \times 3 = 36 \qquad 4 \times 5 + 5 \times 4 = 45$$

3 **20.** Our Geography teacher, Mr Ridge, takes 7 minutes to mark each pupil's test. He has a class of 32.

   How many minutes marking will he save if nine of the class are absent?

Multiples and remainders

Exercise 2

1. **1.** Which of the following five calculations gives a multiple of 5?

    $1 \times 2 + 3 + 4$ $1 + 2 \times 3 + 4$ $1 \times 2 + 3 \times 4$ $1 + 2 \times 3 \times 4$
    $1 \times 2 \times 3 \times 4$

1. **2.** What is the remainder when $2\,400\,040\,002$ is divided by 5?

2. **3.** How many of the following five integers are multiples of 3?

    123   234   345   456   567

2. **4.** Which of the following five numbers is exactly divisible by 7?

    104   106   108   110   112

3. **5.** What is the remainder when $354\,972$ is divided by 7?

4. **6.** Which of the following five numbers is three less than a multiple of 5 and three more than a multiple of 6?

    12   17   21   22   27

4. **7.** What is the remainder when $7\,000\,010$ is divided by 7?

5 **8.** Which of the following five numbers is divisible by 7?

$$111 \quad 1111 \quad 11\,111 \quad 111\,111 \quad 1\,111\,111$$

5 **9.** The word 'thirty' contains 6 letters and $30 = 5 \times 6$. Similarly, the word 'forty' contains 5 letters and $40 = 8 \times 5$.

Which of the following is not a multiple of the number of letters it contains?

$$\text{six} \quad \text{twelve} \quad \text{eighteen} \quad \text{seventy} \quad \text{ninety}$$

5 **10.** How many of the following five numbers are multiples of 5?

$$1 \quad 2 \quad 3 \quad 4 \quad 5$$

7 **11.** Which of the following five numbers is not a multiple of 3?

$$12 \quad 234 \quad 3456 \quad 45\,678 \quad 567\,890$$

8 **12.** Which of the following five numbers has the same remainder when it is divided by 2 as when it is divided by 3?

$$3 \quad 5 \quad 7 \quad 9 \quad 11$$

8 **13.** I saw the following five numbers on cars on the way to school. Each number, with one exception, has the same remainder when divided by 9.

Which is the exception?

$$113 \quad 257 \quad 554 \quad 725 \quad 861$$

11 **14.** Which of the following five statements is false?

12 is a multiple of 2   123 is a multiple of 3
1234 is a multiple of 4   12 345 is a multiple of 5
123 456 is a multiple of 6

Miscellany 1

Exercise 3

1. What is two and thirty-four hundredths when written as a decimal?

2. Which of the following five diagrams could be drawn without taking the pen off the page and without drawing along a line already drawn?

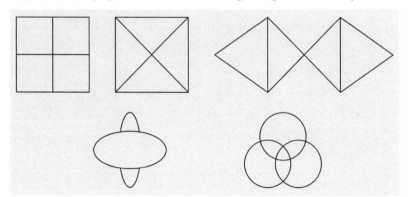

3. Horatio the hamster likes to eat parts of clock faces.

   In which of the following five clock faces has the largest sum of numbers been eaten?

4. The diagram shows six small squares made with matchsticks.

   How many matchsticks need to be removed to leave precisely three small squares that touch only at corners?

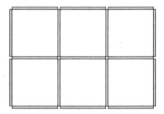

5. Among the children in a certain family, each child has at least one brother and at least one sister.

   What is the *smallest* possible number of children in the family?

6. Which of the following five bar charts could represent the data from the pie chart on the right?

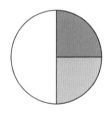

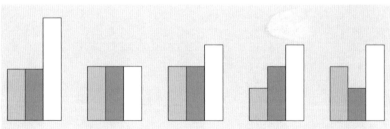

4   **7.** In this partly completed pyramid, each small rectangle is to contain the sum of the two numbers in the small rectangles immediately below it.

What number should replace *n*?

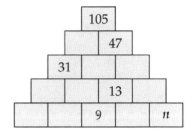

4   **8.** Which of the following five points is *not* at a distance of 1 unit from the origin?

$$(0,1) \quad (1,0) \quad (0,-1) \quad (-1,0) \quad (1,1)$$

4   **9.** Sam has six plain-coloured plates hanging on her living-room wall, in the formation shown.

What is the smallest number of plates that need to be moved to turn this formation upside down?

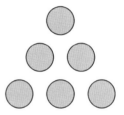

5   **10.** In the diagram, the small squares are all the same size.

What fraction of the large square is shaded?

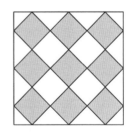

6   **11.** Each block shown in this tower is to have a number displayed on it. Some are already done. For each block above the bottom row, the number on it should be the sum of the numbers on the two blocks it stands upon.

What number should replace *n*?

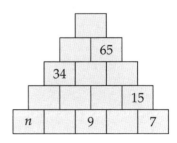

6 **12.** The network illustrates the relative
ages of five children Uo, Ko, Jo, Mo,
and Co.

The arrow from U to K means that Uo
is older than Ko.

What is the correct order of ages,
youngest first?

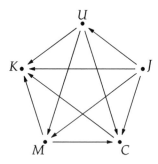

7 **13.** A guinea-pig in a large field is tethered to one end of a 10 metre rope.
The other end of the rope is attached to a ring which is free to slide
along a fixed horizontal rail, 10 metres long, in the middle of the field.

Which of the following five diagrams shows the shape of the part of
the field that the guinea-pig can reach?

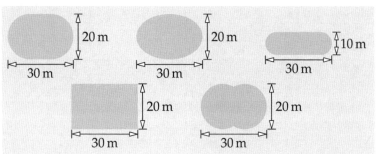

7 **14.** The Mystery Prize at the Bank of England Christmas Party was a pile
of crisp new £5 notes, numbered from 659 384 up to 659 500.

What was the value of the prize?

8 **15.** Two identical rulers are placed together, as shown.

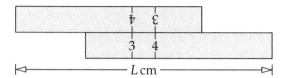

Each ruler is exactly 10 cm long and is marked in centimetres from 0 to 10. The 3 cm mark on each ruler is aligned with the 4 cm mark on the other. The overall length is L cm.

What is the value of L?

8 **16.** The diagram shows two circles enclosed in a rectangle measuring 9 cm × 5 cm.

What is the distance between the centres of the circles?

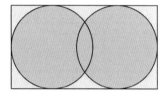

8 **17.** A single piece of string is threaded through five holes in a piece of card. One side of the card is shown in the diagram on the right.

Which of the following five diagrams could *not* represent the pattern of the string on the reverse side?

8 **18.** I owe fifty-five people £55 each. In my piggy bank I have fifty £50 notes and five £5 notes.

Is there enough in my piggy bank to pay all my debts?

9 **19.** The diagram shows the positions of
    four people (each marked ✗) in a
    room in an Art Gallery.

    In the middle of the room is a stone
    column.

    Ali can see none of the other three
    people.

    Bea can see only Caz.

    Caz can see Bea and Dan.

    Dan can see only Caz.

    Who is at position *P*?

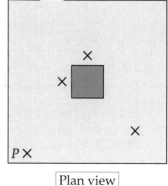

Plan view

9 **20.** Three-quarters of the junior members of a tennis club are boys and
    the rest are girls.

    What is the ratio of boys to girls among these members?

Time and dates

Exercise 4

1. Last Saturday, each half of a hockey match lasted 40 minutes and the half-time interval was a quarter of an hour. The match started at 2:30 pm.

   At what time did it finish?

2. It has just turned 22:22.

   How many minutes are there until midnight?

3. How many minutes are there in $\frac{1}{12}$ of a day?

4. My train was scheduled to leave at 17:40 and to arrive at 18:20.

   However, it started five minutes late and the journey took 42 minutes. At what time did I arrive?

5. Sir Isaac Newton, the English mathematician, physicist and discoverer of the laws of gravity, was born in Woolsthorpe, Lincolnshire in 1642, the same year that Galileo, the Italian scientist, died.

   How many years before 2000 was that?

6. An oak was planted to mark the birth of Oliver Albert King. He died in 1911 aged 62.

   How old was the tree in 1998?

3 **7.** Gollum eats fish on alternate days.

Which of the following five phrases states how often he eats fish on a Monday?

twice a day   once a week   once a fortnight

once a month   once a year

3 **8.** The theme music for the famous science-fiction film *2001: A Space Odyssey* is taken from *Also Sprach Zarathustra*, which was written by Richard Strauss in 1896.

How many years was that before the film itself was produced in 1968?

4 **9.** In January 1859, an eight-year-old boy dropped a newly-hatched eel into a well in Sweden (apparently in order to keep the water free of insects). The eel, named Åle, finally died in August 2014.

How many years old was Åle when it died?

5 **10.** One of the mascots for the 2012 Olympic Games was called 'Wenlock' because the town of Wenlock in Shropshire first held the Wenlock Olympian Games in 1850.

How many years before 2012 was that?

5 **11.** A 'Supertape' plays for 6 hours. It rewinds 18 times as quickly as it plays.

How many minutes does it take to rewind a Supertape completely?

5 **12.** My train was scheduled to leave at 17:42 and to arrive at 18:17.

However, it started four minutes late, and the journey took 43 minutes.

At what time did I arrive?

7 **13.** How many minutes are there from 11:11 until 23:23 on the same day?

7 **14.** Today, the sun rose at Greenwich at 6:45 am and will set 12 hours and 44 minutes later.

At what time will the sun set at Greenwich today?

9 **15.** Which of the following five periods of time is the longest?

> 3002 hours   125 days $17\frac{1}{2}$ weeks   4 months
>
> $\frac{1}{4}$ of a year

12 **16.** The musical *Rent* contains a song that starts "Five hundred and twenty five thousand six hundred minutes".

Which of the following is closest to this length of time?

> a week   a year   a decade   a century   a millennium

12 **17.** The White Rabbit has an appointment to see the Red Queen at 4 pm every day apart from weekends.

On Monday, he arrives 16 minutes late. Each day after that he hurries more and more and so manages to halve the amount of time that he arrives late each day.

On what day of the week does he arrive just 15 seconds late?

13 **18.** According to a newspaper report, marine experts at the Sea Life Centre in Brighton are teaching an octopus to open jam-jars to get at food as a way of stopping it becoming bored.

The octopus opens four jars simultaneously and each jar takes 30 seconds to open.

How many jars does the octopus open per hour?

14 **19.** In 2010 the Severn Bridge had carried just over 300 million vehicles since it was opened in 1966.

Over that time, which of the following is approximately the average number of vehicles per day?

> 600   2000   6000   20 000   60 000

Spatial problems

Exercise 5

1. **1.** How many letters of the word MATHEMATICS do not have any lines of symmetry?

2. **2.** Each letter in the acronym shown alongside is rotated through 90° clockwise. **U K M T**

   Which of the following could be the result?

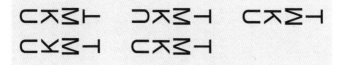

3. **3.** How many of the six faces of a die (shown below) have fewer than three lines of symmetry?

2 **4.** The diagram shows a pattern made from matchsticks stuck to a piece of card.

   What is the smallest number of matchsticks that need to be added so that the resulting pattern has a line of symmetry?

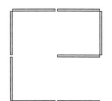

3 **5.** A wall clock (with hour marks, but no numbers) shows the time as half past ten.

   When the clock is seen reflected in a vertical mirror, which of the following five times does it appear to show?

   half past one   4 o'clock   2:30   eight hundred hours
   just gone 7 minutes past six

4 **6.** Beatrix looks at the word JUNIOR in a mirror.

   How many of the reflected letters never look the same as the original, no matter how Beatrix holds the mirror?

4 **7.** You look in a mirror at an accurate clock at 1:30 pm.

   Which of the following diagrams could you see?

5 **8.** The diagram shows a weaver's design for a *rihlèlò*, a winnowing tray from Mozambique.

   How many lines of symmetry does the design have?

5 **9.** Which of the following could be the image of U K M T when seen reflected in a mirror?

ПKWⱢ   TMKU   UꓘMT   ПꓘWⱢ   ⱢWꓘП

6 **10.** Jonny's rat is a slow learner! Every time it goes through this maze, it visits every square at least once.

What is the smallest possible number of squares it visits more than once when it goes through the maze?

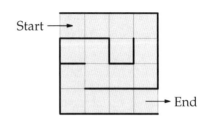

9 **11.** Beatrix takes a sheet of paper (shown on the left of the diagram), folds the sheet in half 4 times and punches a hole all the way through the folded sheet, as shown on the right. She then unfolds the sheet.

How many holes are there now in the unfolded sheet?

10 **12.** A square is folded exactly in half and then in half again.

Which of the following five shapes could *not* be the resulting shape?

11 **13.** The diagram shows a rod with five equally spaced points *A, B, C, D* and *E* marked on it.

The rod is rotated three times through 180 degrees, first about *A*, then about *B* and finally about *E*.

Which point finishes in the same position as it was at the start?

12 **14.** Laura wishes to cut this shape, which is made up of nine small squares, into pieces that she can then rearrange to make a 3 × 3 square.

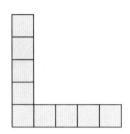

What is the smallest number of pieces that she needs to cut the shape into so that she can do this?

12 **15.** Along which line should an upright mirror be placed so that the part of the square on one side of the mirror and its reflection form an octagon?

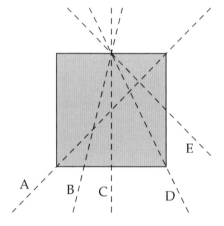

13 **16.** A rectangle *PQRS* is cut into two pieces along *PX*, where *PX* = *XR* and *PS* = *SX*, as shown.

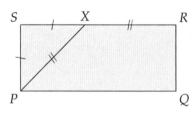

The two pieces are reassembled without turning either piece over, by matching two sides of equal length.

Not counting the original rectangle, how many different shapes are possible?

15 **17.** What is the smallest number of *additional* cells that need to be shaded in this 5 × 5 grid, in order for the figure to have at least one line of symmetry *and* rotational symmetry of order 2?

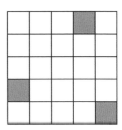

Units

Exercise 6

2   **1.** A comb for horses has 100 teeth, each
     1 mm wide. The gaps between the
     teeth are also 1 mm wide.

     How many centimetres long is the
     comb?

2   **2.** Which of the following is roughly equal to 200 ml?

     a thimbleful   a spoonful   a cupful   a saucepanful
     a bucketful

3   **3.** Which of the following five items could have a length of 2010 mm?

     a table   an oil tanker   a teaspoon   a school hall
     a hen's egg

4   **4.** The world's largest coin, made by the Royal Mint of Canada, was
     auctioned in June 2010.

     The coin has mass 100 kg; a standard British £1 coin has mass 10 g.

     What sum of money in £1 coins has the same mass as the record-
     breaking coin?

5   **5.** At Spuds-R-Us, a 2.5 kg bag of potatoes costs £1.25.

How much would one tonne of potatoes cost?

7   **6.** Which of the following five distances is closest to 1.2 km?

0.75 miles   1 mile   1.2 miles   1.6 miles   1.9 miles

[A distance of 8 km is approximately 5 miles.]

7   **7.** Peter Piper picked a peck of pickled peppers. 1 peck $= \frac{1}{4}$ bushel and 1 bushel $= \frac{1}{9}$ barrel.

How many *more* pecks does Peter Piper need to pick to fill a barrel?

7   **8.** King Harry's arm is twice as long as his forearm, which is twice as long as his hand, which is twice as long as his middle finger, which is twice as long as his thumb.

His new bed is as long as four arms. How many thumbs length is that?

7   **9.** The lightest seeds in the world are probably those of the Creeping Lady's-tresses Orchid, 500 000 of which would weigh 1 gram.

How many millions of these seeds weigh 1 kilogram?

7   **10.** In music, a demisemiquaver is half of half of half a crotchet, and there are four crotchets in a semibreve.

How many demisemiquavers are there in a semibreve?

10   **11.** In 2000, each Junior Mathematical Challenge answer sheet weighed 6 grams and 140 000 pupils entered the Challenge.

How many kilograms did all their answer sheets weigh altogether?

10   **12.** Each day throughout July 1995 I picked 300 g of raspberries from my garden.

Which of the following five weights is equal to the total weight of the raspberries that I picked that month?

10 g   9 kg   9.3 kg   10 kg   9300 kg

13 **13.** When painting the living-room, I used half of a 3 litre can to complete the first coat of paint. I then used two thirds of what was left to complete the second coat.

How many millilitres of paint were left after both coats were complete?

14 **14.** Which of the following five lengths is equal to one million millimetres?

$$1\,m \qquad 10\,m \qquad 100\,m \qquad 1\,km \qquad 10\,km$$

15 **15.** An active sphagnum bog deposits a depth of about 1 metre of peat per 1000 years.

Which of the following is roughly the number of millimetres deposited per day?

$$0.0003 \qquad 0.003 \qquad 0.03 \qquad 0.3 \qquad 3$$

Fractions and percentages

Exercise 7

3   **1.** What is the value of $\dfrac{12\,345}{1+2+3+4+5}$?

3   **2.** All of the Forty Thieves were light-fingered, but only two of them were caught red-handed.

What percentage is that?

3   **3.** Which of the following five calculations has the biggest value?

$\frac{1}{2}$ of 24 $\frac{1}{3}$ of 36 $\frac{1}{4}$ of 60 $\frac{1}{5}$ of 50 $\frac{1}{6}$ of 84

4   **4.** What is 40% of 50% of £60?

5   **5.** What is the value of $\dfrac{1}{25} + 0.25$?

5   **6.** The difference between $\dfrac{1}{3}$ of a certain number and $\dfrac{1}{4}$ of the same number is 3.

What is that number?

5   **7.** All that Old Mother Hubbard had in her cupboard was a Giant Bear chocolate bar.

She gave each of her children one-twelfth of the chocolate bar. One third of the bar was left.

How many children did she have?

6   **8.** Which of the following five expressions has the largest value?

$$6 \div \frac{1}{2} \qquad 5 \div \frac{1}{3} \qquad 4 \div \frac{1}{4} \qquad 3 \div \frac{1}{5} \qquad 2 \div \frac{1}{6}$$

6   **9.** When the following five fractions are put in their correct places on the number line, which fraction is in the middle?

$$-\frac{1}{7} \qquad \frac{1}{6} \qquad \frac{1}{5} \qquad \frac{1}{4} \qquad -\frac{1}{3}$$

6   **10.** Which of the following five fractions has a value nearer to one than the other four?

$$\frac{12}{23} \qquad \frac{23}{34} \qquad \frac{34}{45} \qquad \frac{45}{56} \qquad \frac{56}{67}$$

8   **11.** What is the value of

$$\frac{2+4+6+8+10+12+14+16+18+20}{1+2+3+4+5+6+7+8+9+10}?$$

8   **12.** Tommy Thomas's tankard holds 480 ml when it is one quarter empty. How much does it hold when it is one quarter full?

9   **13.** Which of the following five expressions has the smallest value?

$$\frac{1}{2}-\frac{1}{3} \qquad \frac{1}{3}-\frac{1}{4} \qquad \frac{1}{4}-\frac{1}{5} \qquad \frac{1}{5}-\frac{1}{6} \qquad \frac{1}{6}-\frac{1}{7}$$

9   **14.** What is the value of $\dfrac{4}{1-\frac{3}{4}}$?

10 **15.** Which of the following five expressions has the largest value?

$$\frac{1}{2}+\frac{1}{3} \qquad \frac{1}{2}-\frac{1}{4} \qquad \frac{1}{2}\times\frac{1}{4} \qquad \frac{1}{2}\div\frac{1}{4} \qquad \frac{1}{4}\div\frac{1}{2}$$

11 **16.** In 1833 a ship arrived in Calcutta with 120 tons remaining of its cargo of ice

One third of the original cargo was lost because it had melted on the voyage.

How many tons of ice was the ship carrying when it set sail?

11 **17.** Which of the following five fractions has the smallest value?

$$\frac{5}{8} \qquad \frac{6}{13} \qquad \frac{7}{12} \qquad \frac{9}{17} \qquad \frac{10}{19}$$

12 **18.** Gill was 21 in 2009. At the famous visit to the clinic in 1988, her weight was calculated to be 5 kg, but in 2009 she weighed 50 kg.

What was the percentage increase in Gill's weight from 1988 to 2009?

13 **19.** At a certain school, 48% of the pupils are girls; 25% of the girls and 50% of the boys travel to school by bus.

What percentage of the whole school travel by bus?

14 **20.** A bottle contains 750 ml of mineral water. Rachel drinks 50% more than Ross, and these two friends finish the bottle between them.

How much does Rachel drink?

Digits

Exercise 8

1. What is the smallest four-digit positive integer which has four different digits?

2. The year 2004 has the units digit equal to twice the thousands digit. How many years after 2004 will it be before this next happens?

3. What is the difference between the smallest 4-digit integer and the largest 3-digit integer?

4. Yesterday, the reading on Granny's electricity meter was 098 657. She was shocked to realise that all six of these digits are different.

   How many more units of electricity will she use before the next time all the digits are different?

5. Mr Owens wants to keep the students quiet during a Mathematics lesson. He asks them to multiply all the numbers from 1 to 99 together and then tell him the last-but-one digit of the result.

   What is the correct answer?

6. The sum of seven single-digit positive integers is 17.

   Six of these numbers are equal.

   What is the seventh number?

9　**7.** What is the smallest possible difference between two different nine-digit integers, each of which includes all of the digits 1 to 9?

9　**8.** How many different digits appear when $\dfrac{20}{11}$ is written as a recurring decimal?

10　**9.** The digit 4 is replaced by the digit 3 in each of the following five numbers.

$$45\,678 \qquad 87\,654 \qquad 95\,400 \qquad 74\,000 \qquad 99\,949$$

Which number is reduced by the largest amount?

11　**10.** The digits of 2000 add up to 2.

In how many *other* years between year 1 and year 2000 did the digits add up to 2?

12　**11.** In this subtraction, *P*, *Q*, *R*, *S* and *T* represent single digits.

What is the value of $P + Q + R + S + T$?

$$
\begin{array}{r}
7\ Q\ 2\ S\ T \\
-\ P\ 3\ R\ 9\ 6 \\
\hline
2\ 2\ 2\ 2\ 2
\end{array}
$$

13　**12.** The number 2002 is a palindrome, since it reads the same forwards and backwards.

For how many *other* years this century, after 2002, is the number of the year a palindrome?

More arithmetic

Exercise 9

3   **1.** In my row in the theatre the seats are numbered consecutively from T1 to T50. I am sitting in seat T17 and you are sitting in seat T39.

How many seats are there between us?

4   **2.** The number $987\,654\,321$ is multiplied by 9.

How many times does the digit 8 occur in the result?

4   **3.** Which of the following five calculations gives the largest answer?

$$(1 \times 2) \times (3 \times 4) \qquad (1 \times 2) + (3 \times 4) \qquad (1 \times 2) \times (3 + 4)$$
$$(1 + 2) \times (3 \times 4) \qquad (1 + 2) \times (3 + 4)$$

4   **4.** Which of the following five expressions gives the largest number?

$$1 \times 9 + 9 \times 7 \qquad 1 + 9 + 9 + 7 \qquad 1 \times 9 + 9 + 7 \qquad 1 + 9 \times 9 + 7$$
$$1 + 9 + 9 \times 7$$

5   **5.** Which of the following five numbers is *not* the difference between two of the others?

$$1 \quad 7 \quad 6 \quad 5 \quad 2$$

6   **6.** What is the value of $\left((1-1)-1\right) - \left(1-(1-1)\right)$?

6   **7.** What is the value of $101 + 2002 + 30\,003 + 400\,004 + 5\,000\,005$?

6   **8.** To help sell his house, Southampton butcher Simon Broadribb offered
     to give the buyer meat worth £20 every week for one year; this could
     be either 40 burgers, or 96 sausages, or 140 rashers of bacon, or 30
     lamb cutlets, or 35 portions of mince.

     Based on that offer, which of the following five items is the most
     expensive?

     > a burger   a sausage   a rasher of bacon   a lamb cutlet
     > a portion of mince

7   **9.** The result of the calculation $123\,456\,789 \times 8$ is almost the same as
     $987\,654\,321$ except that two of the digits are in a different order.

     What is the sum of these two digits?

7   **10.** What is the value of $2014 - 4102$?

7   **11.** A small ink cartridge has enough ink to print 600 pages. Three small
     cartridges can print as many pages as two medium cartridges. Three
     medium cartridges can print as many pages as two large cartridges.

     How many pages can be printed using a large cartridge?

8   **12.** What is the difference between the largest and smallest of the following
     five numbers?

     > 0.89   0.9   0.17   0.72   0.73

9   **13.** One of the three symbols $+$, $-$, $\times$ is inserted somewhere between the
     digits of 2016 to give a new number. For example, $20 - 16$ gives 4.

     How many of the following four numbers can be obtained in this
     way?

     > 36   195   207   320

9 **14.** Four of the following five calculations give the same answer.

$$2 \times \sqrt{64} \qquad 22 - 2 \times 3 \qquad 2^4 \qquad 5^2 - 3^2 \qquad 4 + 4 \times 2$$

Which is the odd one out?

10 **15.** In the expression $1 \heartsuit 2 \heartsuit 3 \heartsuit 4$ each $\heartsuit$ is to be replaced by either $+$ or $\times$.

What is the largest value of all the expressions that can be obtained in this way?

10 **16.** Correct to one decimal place, what is the square root of 18?

11 **17.** In the following expression, each $\heartsuit$ is to be replaced with either $+$ or $-$ in such a way that the result of the calculation is 100.

$$123 \heartsuit 45 \heartsuit 67 \heartsuit 89$$

The number of $+$ signs used is p and the number of $-$ signs used is m. What is the value of $p - m$?

12 **18.** Which one of the following five statements is *false*?

$$4 \times 5 + 67 = 45 + 6 \times 7 \qquad 3 \times 7 + 48 = 37 + 4 \times 8$$
$$6 \times 3 + 85 = 63 + 8 \times 5 \qquad 2 \times 5 + 69 = 25 + 6 \times 9$$
$$9 \times 6 + 73 = 96 + 7 \times 3$$

14 **19.** In the sequence 2, 3, 5, 10, ..., each number after the second is the sum of all the previous numbers in the sequence.

What is the 10th number in the sequence?

15 **20.** It was reported recently that, in an average lifetime of 70 years, each human is likely to swallow about 8 spiders while sleeping.

The population of the UK is around 60 million.

Which of the following is closest to the number of unfortunate spiders consumed in this way in the UK each year?

$$50\,000 \qquad 600\,000 \qquad 7\,000\,000 \qquad 80\,000\,000 \qquad 900\,000\,000$$

Algebra

Exercise 10

2 **1.** On holiday last year Phil Atterlist bought ten postcards for 10p each and ten second class stamps at 19p each.

How much change did Phil get from £10?

3 **2.** What is the value of $2 \times 17 + 3 \times 17 + 5 \times 17$?

6 **3.** Gill is now 28 years old and is a teacher of Mathematics at a school that has 600 pupils. There are 30 more girls than boys at the school.

How many girls are at Gill's school?

6 **4.** What is the value of $19 + 99 + 19 \times 99$?

7 **5.** After tennis training, Andy collects twice as many balls as Roger and five more than Maria. They collect 35 balls in total.

How many balls does Andy collect?

8 **6.** Peg has six times as much chocolate as Reg. Meg has twice as much chocolate as Reg.

Peg has how many times as much chocolate as Meg?

9 **7.** Peter has three times as many sisters as brothers. His sister Louise has twice as many sisters as brothers.

How many children are there in the family?

9   **8.** Lisa's bucket does not have a hole in it and weighs 21 kg when full of
       water. After she pours out half the water from the bucket, it weighs
       12 kg.

       What is the weight of the empty bucket?

9   **9.** The symbols *, ●, □ and △ satisfy the following three equations.

$$\triangle + \bullet = *$$
$$\triangle = * + \square$$
$$\triangle + \triangle + \bullet = * + \square + \square$$

Which of the following five expressions is equal to △?

$$* + * \qquad \bullet \qquad \square + \square \qquad * \qquad \square$$

10 **10.** On a journey a certain weight of luggage is carried free, but there is
        a charge of £10 per kilogram for any additional luggage above this
        weight.

        Laa-laa's luggage, which weighs a total of 50 kg, is overweight and
        she is charged £150.

        Po's luggage weighs a total of 30 kg.

        What is the charge for Po's luggage?

12 **11.** A fish weighs a total of 2 kg plus a third of its own weight.

        How may kilograms does the fish weigh?

12 **12.** The symbols ▲, ■, ● and ◆ satisfy the following three equations.

$$\blacktriangle + \blacktriangle = \blacksquare$$
$$\blacksquare + \blacktriangle = \bullet$$
$$\blacklozenge = \bullet + \blacksquare + \blacktriangle$$

How many ▲s are equal to one ◆?

12   **13.** A ball is dropped onto a hard surface. Each time it bounces, it rebounds to exactly one third of the height from which it fell.

After the second bounce the ball rises to a height of 9 cm.

From what height was it originally dropped?

15   **14.** Dilly is 7 years younger than Dally. In 4 years time she will be half Dally's age.

What is the sum of their ages now?

Counting

Exercise 11

3   **1.** A train display shows letters by lighting cells in a grid, such as the letter 'o' shown.

A letter is made bold by also lighting any unlit cell immediately to the right of one in the normal letter.

How many cells are lit in a bold 'o'?

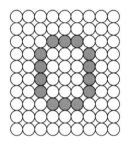

4   **2.** How many triangles of any size are there in this diagram?

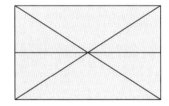

4   **3.** A ladybird has landed at point P on Sam's bow-tie. It travels only along the edges of the bow-tie, but cannot travel along any edge more than once.

How many different ways are there for it to get from P to Q?

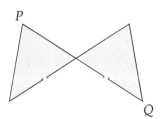

4   **4.** Clearing up after the party I found two pop bottles which were full, two which were one third full, two which were half full, two which were one third empty, two which were half empty, and two which were completely empty.

How many bottles did I find altogether?

5   **5.** The diagram shows a pattern of 16 circles inside a square.

The central circle passes through the points where the other circles touch.

The circles divide the square into regions. How many regions are there?

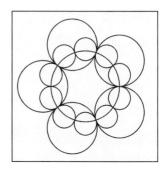

5   **6.** Euclid Gardens has 123 houses in it, numbered consecutively from 1 to 123. Houses 29 to 37 inclusive are knocked down to make space for a multi-storey car park.

How many houses remain in Euclid Gardens?

5   **7.** Kylie the clumsy koala is all fingers and thumbs.

Like all koalas, Kylie has two thumbs and three fingers on each front paw, and one thumb and four fingers on each rear paw.

How many thumbs do Kylie and her nine brothers have between them?

7   **8.** The equilateral triangle XYZ is fixed in position, and divided into four small triangles, as shown.

Two of the four small triangles are to be coloured black and the other two are to be coloured white.

In how many different ways can this be done?

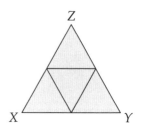

8 **9.** I have two 'Spinners': one is a square; the other is a regular pentagon.

Both spinners are spun at the same time and the two scores obtained are added together.

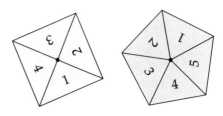

How many different totals are possible?

9 **10.** A 'double-decker' sandwich has three slices of bread and two layers of filling (bread/filling/bread/filling/bread). Each slice of bread has to be buttered on each side that is in contact with the filling.

I make as many of these sandwiches as possible from a sliced loaf which has 22 usable slices, excluding the crusts, which are not used.

How many sides of bread do I have to butter?

10 **11.** The faces of a cube are painted so that any two faces which have an edge in common are painted different colours.

What is the smallest number of colours required?

11 **12.** Nicolas wrote a Christmas card for each of his three sisters—Carol, Holly and Ivy—and put each card into a separate envelope.

In how many different ways can he send a card to each sister so that none of them receives the correct card?

11 **13.** Each face of a cube is to be painted so that 'adjacent' faces (those having an edge in common) never have the same colour. Six different colours of paint are available.

What is the smallest number of colours that need to be used?

12 **14.** How many hexagons are there in the diagram?

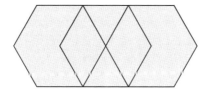

12 **15.** The sheet of paper shown on the left is folded along the dashed lines (each fold being either forwards or backwards) to make the leaflet shown on the right.

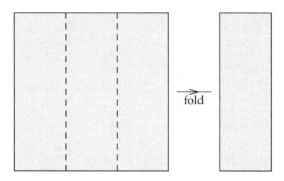

Each of the six 'pages' of the leaflet is printed in a different colour.

No matter how it is folded, the leaflet will have two pages visible on the outside.

How many different pairs of outside pages can be obtained by folding the sheet of paper in different ways?

12 **16.** How many different routes are there from S to T that do not go through either of the points U and V more than once?

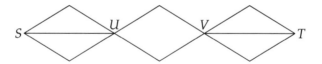

13 **17.** For how many three-digit positive integers is the sum of the digits equal to 25?

14 **18.** The Kings of Clubs, Diamonds, Hearts and Spades, together with their respective Queens, are having an arm-wrestling competition. Everyone wrestles everyone else, except that no King wrestles his own Queen.

How many wrestling bouts are there?

15   **19.** In Matt's pocket there are 8 watermelon jellybeans, 4 vanilla jellybeans
and 4 butter popcorn jellybeans.

What is the smallest number of jellybeans he needs to take out of his
pocket to be certain that he takes at least one of each flavour?

Angles

Exercise 12

3   **1.** What is the value of x?

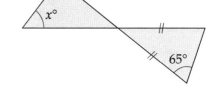

3   **2.** What is the value of x?

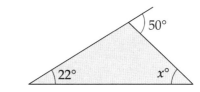

4   **3.** What is the value of x?

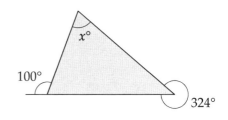

4. The diagram shows a square drawn inside an equilateral triangle.

What is the size of angle *JMC*?

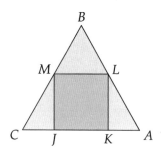

5. What is the value of *x*?

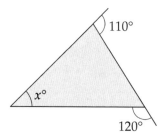

6. What is the sum of the marked angles in the diagram?

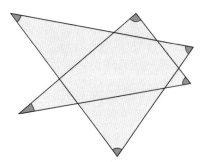

7. What is the value of *x*?

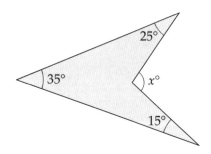

8   **8.** In a triangle with angles $x°$, $y°$ and $z°$
    the average of y and z is x.

    What is the value of x?

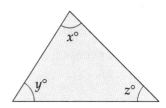

9   **9.** In the diagram on
    the right, *ST* is
    parallel to *UV*.

    What is the value
    of x?

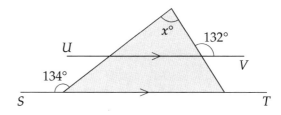

10 **10.** An equilateral triangle is surrounded
    by three squares, as shown.

    What is the value of x?

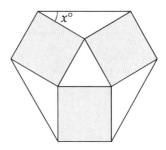

10 **11.** The diagram shows three squares of the
    same size.

    What is the value of x?

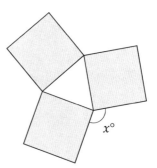

11 **12.** The diagram shows an equilateral triangle inside a rectangle.

What is the value of $x + y$?

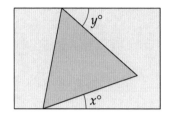

12 **13.** What is the value of x?

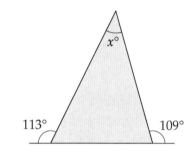

13 **14.** The diagram shows two equal squares.

What is the value of x?

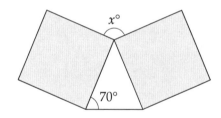

13 **15.** In the triangle PQR, the angle RPQ is $40°$ and the internal bisectors of the angles at Q and R meet at S, as shown.

What is the size of angle RSQ?

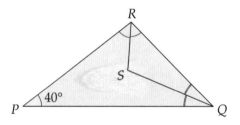

13 **16.** In the diagram, angle *RPM* is 20°
   and angle *QMP* is 70°.

   What is the value of angle *PRS*?

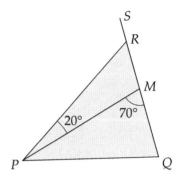

14 **17.** In the diagram, *AB* = *AC* and *D* is
   a point on *AC* such that *BD* = *BC*.
   Also, angle *BAC* is 40°.

   What is the size of angle *ABD* ?

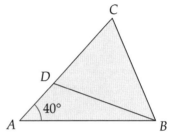

15 **18.** The diagram alongside shows a rectangular envelope
   made by folding (and gluing) a single piece of paper.

   Which of the following five diagrams could show the
   original unfolded piece of paper? (The dotted lines are
   the fold lines.)

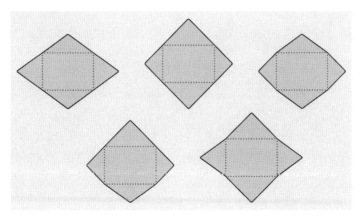

Reasoning

Exercise 13

6 **1.** The largest of the rectangles below is red and the smallest is blue. Orange is the same size as yellow and not next to blue.

Which rectangle is orange?

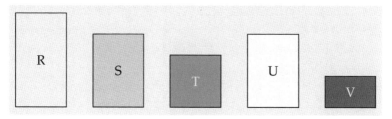

6 **2.** Which of the following five letters does not occur at all in this sentence?

a   b   c   d   e

7 **3.** In California, a bottle of orange juice costs $3, but when you return the bottle you get $2 back.

What is the largest number of bottles of juice you can buy if you start with $10?

7   **4.** Mary has three brothers and four sisters. They all (including Mary) buy each other an Easter egg.

How many eggs are bought?

8   **5.** Amy, Ben and Chris are standing in a row. Amy is to the left of Ben and Chris is to the right of Amy.

Which of the following five statements is necessarily true?

> Ben is furthest to the left.   Chris is furthest to the right.
> Amy is in the middle.   Amy is furthest to the left.
> None of the other four statements is true.

10   **6.** On Monday last week Dilly started to learn the Tlingit language. Every day she learnt five new words, but when she woke every morning she had forgotten two of the words learnt the day before.

On which day did Dilly first achieve her target of learning fourteen words?

11   **7.** The *Pythagoras School of Music* has 100 students. Of these, 60 are in the band and 20 are in the orchestra, and 12 students are in both the band and the orchestra.

How many students are in neither the band nor the orchestra?

12   **8.**   This sentence contains the letter e ❀ times.

How many of the following five words can replace ❀ to make the sentence above true?

> seven   eight   nine   ten   eleven

14   **9.** The diagram shows four empty glasses with their bases at the bottom. One move consists of turning over exactly three of the four glasses.

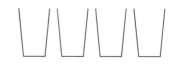

What is the smallest number of moves needed before all of the glasses have their bases at the top?

Averages and rates

Exercise 14

2   **1.** Heidi is 2.1 m tall, while Lola is only 1.4 m tall.
What is their average height?

4   **2.** Gill went for a five-hour walk. Her average speed was between 3 km/h and 4 km/h.
Which of the following five distances could be the distance she walked?

| 12 km | 14 km | 19 km | 24 km | 35 km |

9   **3.** According to a newspaper report, "A 63-year-old man has rowed around the world without leaving his living-room." He clocked up 25 048 miles on a rowing machine that he received for his 50th birthday.
To one significant figure, how many miles per year has he rowed since he was given the machine?

9   **4.** The average age of the four members of 'All Sinners' boy band is 19.
What is the average age when an extra member who is 24 years old joins them?

11   **5.** Usain runs twice as fast as his mum. His mum runs five times as fast as his pet tortoise, Turbo.

They all set off together for a run down the same straight path.

When Usain has run 100 m, how far apart are his mum and Turbo the tortoise?

12   **6.** The six-member squad for the Ladybirds five-a-side team consists of a 2-spot ladybird, a 10-spot, a 14-spot, an 18-spot, a 24-spot and a pine ladybird (on the bench).

The average number of spots for members of the squad is 12.

How many spots has the pine ladybird?

13   **7.** What is the average of $\dfrac{2}{3}$ and $\dfrac{4}{9}$?

13   **8.** The sum of ten consecutive integers is 5.

What is the largest of these integers?

14   **9.** Karen was given a mark of 72 for Mayhematics. Her average mark for Mayhematics and Mathemagics was 78.

What was her mark for Mathemagics?

15   **10.** It is well known that the Pobble has no toes, and that the three-toed sloth has 12 toes (3 on each of its 4 feet).

A synchronised swimming team is made up of 7 Pobbles and 5 three-toed sloths.

What is the average number of toes per team member?

Areas and perimeters

Exercise 15

6   **1.** The diagram shows a square divided into strips of equal width. Three strips are grey and two are black.

What fraction of the perimeter of the square is black?

6   **2.** Each square in the diagram is 1 cm × 1 cm.

What is the area of triangle ABM, in cm^2?

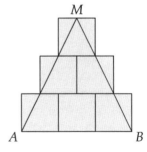

6   **3.** The diagram shows a single floor tile in which the sides of the outer square have length 8 cm and those of the inner square have length 6 cm.

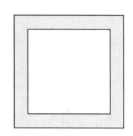

Adam Ant walks once around the perimeter of the inner square and Annabel Ant walks once around the perimeter of the outer square.

How much further does Annabel walk than Adam?

8   **4.** A square is divided into three congruent rectangles. The middle rectangle is removed and replaced on one side of the original square to form an octagon, as shown.

What is the ratio of the length of the perimeter of the square to the length of the perimeter of the octagon?

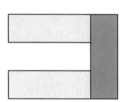

8   **5.** The diagram shows an arrangement of ten square tiles.

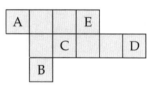

Which labelled tile could be removed, but still leave the length of the perimeter unchanged?

8   **6.** The shape in the diagram is made up of three rectangles, each measuring 3 cm × 1 cm.

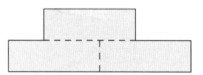

What is the length of the perimeter of the shape?

9 **7.** Triangles *XYZ* and *PQR* are drawn on a square grid.

What fraction of the area of triangle *XYZ* is the area of triangle *PQR*?

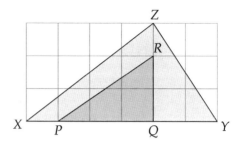

9 **8.** In the diagram, a corner of the shaded star is at the midpoint of each side of the large square.

What fraction of the large square is covered by the star?

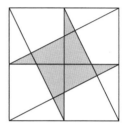

10 **9.** The diagram shows two arrows drawn on separate 4 cm × 4 cm grids.

One arrow points north and the other points west.

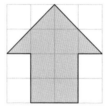
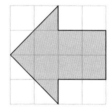

When the two arrows are drawn on the same 4 cm × 4 cm grid (still pointing north and west) they overlap. What is the area of overlap?

11 **10.** In the diagram shown, all the angles are right angles and all the sides are of length 1 cm, 2 cm or 3 cm.

What is the area of the shaded region, in cm²?

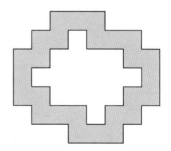

11. My rabbit Nibbles lives in a movable pen and helps to keep the grass short.

The rectangular pen measures 2 m × 3 m, and is oriented as shown. On successive days, the pen is moved 1 m east, 2 m south, 1 m west and 2 m north.

What is the total area of the region of grass which Nibbles can nibble?

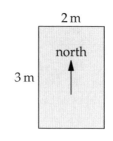

12. Four 10 cm × 1 cm rectangular paper strips are laid flat on a table. Each strip is at right angles to two of the other strips as shown.

What is the area of the table covered by the strips?

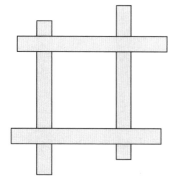

13. A rectangle is split into triangles by drawing its diagonals, as shown.

What is the ratio of the area of triangle P to the area of triangle Q?

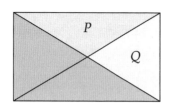

14. Each side of an isosceles triangle is a whole number of centimetres long. Its perimeter has length 20 cm.

How many possibilities are there for the lengths of its sides?

15. The line alongside is 0.2 mm thick. _____

How many metres long would the line need to be to cover an area of one square metre?

14 **16.** In the rules of association football, Law 1 states that the field of play should be rectangular and have length from 100 to 130 yards, and width from 50 to 100 yards.

How many more square yards is the area of the largest possible field of play than the area of the smallest possible field of play?

14 **17.** How much smaller is the area of a 60 cm × 40 cm rectangle than that of a square with the same perimeter?

15 **18.** A 6 cm × 8 cm and a 9 cm × 7 cm rectangle overlap with one corner coinciding, as shown.

What is the area of the region *outside* the overlap?

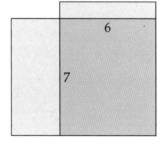

Integers

Exercise 16

3   **1.** Which of the following five numbers has exactly one factor other than 1 and itself?

$$6 \quad 8 \quad 13 \quad 19 \quad 25$$

5   **2.** For £2, a stamp machine gives a mixture of 20p and 26p stamps worth a total of £2.02.

How many 20p stamps are included?

6   **3.** A transport company's vans each carry a maximum load of 12 tonnes. A firm needs to deliver 24 crates each weighing 5 tonnes.

What is the smallest number of van loads needed to do this?

8   **4.** How many prime numbers are there in the following list?

$$1 \quad 12 \quad 123 \quad 1234 \quad 12\,345 \quad 123\,456$$

8   **5.** What is the sum of all the different prime factors of 1998?

9 **6.** The Bean family are very particular about beans. At every meal all Beans eat some beans. Pa Bean always eats more beans than Ma Bean but never eats more than half the beans. Ma Bean always eats the same number of beans as both children together and the two children always eat the same number of beans as each other.

At their last meal they ate 23 beans altogether.

How many beans did Pa Bean eat?

10 **7.** When Harry bought his train ticket he received £2.50 in change. He noticed that for each coin in his change there was exactly one other coin of the same value.

What was the coin of smallest value in Harry's change?

11 **8.** What is the smallest prime number that is the sum of three different prime numbers?

11 **9.** What is the sum of all the prime numbers which are less than 25?

12 **10.** Sir Lance has a lot of tables and chairs in his house. Each rectangular table seats eight people and each round table seats five people.

What is the smallest number of tables he will need to use to seat 35 guests and himself, without any of the seating around these tables remaining unoccupied?

13 **11.** In the diagram, each line joining two numbers is to be labelled with the sum of the two numbers that are at its end points.

How many of these labels are multiples of 3?

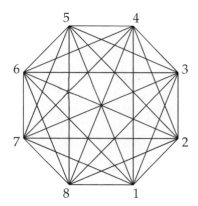

13 **12.** In the multiplication table on the right, the input factors (in the first row and the first column) are all missing and only some of the products within the table have been given.

What is the value of

$$P + Q + R + S + T?$$

×					
	P	10		20	
	15	Q	40		
	18		R	60	
		20		S	24
			56		T

13 **13.** At the end of a hard day at the mine, the Seven Dwarves share out all their gold nuggets, making sure that they each get the same number of nuggets. Any that are left over are given to Snow White.

Which of the following five numbers of nuggets would leave Snow White with the most?

300   400   500   600   700

13 **14.** Since 2003 is a prime number, 2003 is a 'prime year'.

In the next ten years after 2003 there is just one 'prime year'. Which is it?

14 **15.** Digits on a calculator are represented by a number of illuminated bars. The digits and the bars which represent them are shown in the diagram.

How many digits are both prime and represented by a prime number of illuminated bars?

15 **16.** Which of the following five expressions is divisible by all of the integers from 1 to 10 inclusive?

23×34 34×45 45×56 56×67 67×78

15 **17.** I choose three numbers from this number square, including one number from each row and one number from each column. I then multiply the three numbers together.

1	2	3
4	5	6
7	8	9

What is the largest possible product?

15 **18.** There are six different three-digit positive integers, each of which contains all the digits 1, 3 and 5.

How many of these three-digit numbers are prime?

Miscellany 2

Exercise 17

10 **1.** On standard dice the total number of pips on each pair of opposite faces is 7.

Two standard dice are placed in a stack, as shown, so that the total number of pips on the two touching faces is 5.

What is the total number of pips on the top and bottom faces of the stack?

10 **2.** You want to draw the shape in the diagram without taking your pen off the paper and without going over any line more than once.

Where should you start?

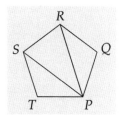

10 **3.** At the Marldon Apple-Pie-Fayre bake-off, prize money is awarded for 1st, 2nd and 3rd places in the ratio 3 : 2 : 1.

Last year Mrs Keat and Mr Jewell shared third prize equally.

What fraction of the total prize money did Mrs Keat receive?

10   4. The diagram shows seven identical coins
      placed inside a wooden frame.   The
      coins fit exactly; as a result each coin is
      prevented from sliding.

      What is the largest number of coins that
      may be removed one by one so that, at
      each stage, each remaining coin is still
      unable to slide?

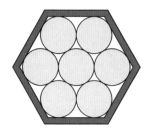

10   5. On the island of Erewhon, all numbers are written with the digits in
      reverse order. For example, twelve is written 21.

      Su Erasmus, an inhabitant of Erewhon, was shown the subtraction
      729 − 45.

      What answer did Su write down (no mistake was made)?

10   6. The digits 0, 1, 2, ... , 9 are equally spaced
      around a circle.

      In the following subtractions each digit is to be
      replaced by the digit exactly opposite it on the
      circle.

      Which subtraction then gives an answer that is
      less than all the others?

              20 − 19   30 − 29   40 − 39   50 − 49   60 − 59

11   7. The first term of a sequence is 1 and the second term is 2. After the
      first two, each of the other terms in the sequence is the sum of all the
      terms which come before it.

      Which of the following five numbers is *not a term* in the sequence?

                      6   24   48   72   96

11   8. In a sequence of numbers, each term after the first three terms is the
      sum of the previous three terms. The first three terms are −3, 0, 2.

      Which is the first term to exceed 100?

11 **9.** A station clock shows each digit by illuminating up to seven bars in a display, as shown.

When all the digits from 0 to 9 are shown in turn, which of the following five diagrams shows the bar that is used least?

11 **10.** Travelling by train from Edinburgh to London, I passed the sign:

London 150 miles

After 7 more miles, I passed another sign:

Edinburgh 250 miles

How far is it by train from Edinburgh to London?

11 **11.** Which one of the sectors in the pie chart represents the mode?

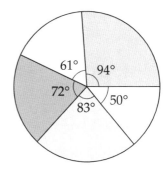

11 **12.** At half time in a netball match, Jokers were leading Jesters by 3 goals to 2. Seven goals were scored in the second half.

Which of the following could *not* have been the result of the match?

the match was drawn   Jesters won by 2 goals
Jesters won by 4 goals   Jokers won by 2 goals
Jokers won by 3 goals

13 **13.** The diagram shows a *Lusona*, a sand picture of the Tshokwe people from the West Central Bantu area of Africa. To draw a Lusona the artist uses a stick to draw a single line in the sand, starting and ending in the same place without lifting the stick in between.

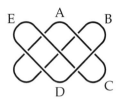

At which point could this Lusona have started?

13 **14.** Points P and Q have coordinates $(1,4)$ and $(1,-2)$ respectively.

For which of the following five coordinates of point R would triangle PQR *not* be isosceles?

$$(-5,4) \qquad (7,1) \qquad (-6,1) \qquad (-6,-2) \qquad (7,-2)$$

14 **15.** The pattern in the box repeats every six symbols.

What are the 100th and 101st symbols, in that order, in the pattern?

14 **16.** The 'disputor' is similar to a calculator, but it behaves a little oddly. When you type in a number, the disputor doubles the number, then reverses the digits of this result, then adds 2 and displays the final result.

I type in a whole number between 10 and 99 inclusive.

Which of the following numbers could be the final result displayed?

$$39 \quad 41 \quad 42 \quad 43 \quad 45$$

15 **17.** How many of the following four expressions are squares?

$$1^3 + 2^3 \qquad 1^3 + 2^3 + 3^3 \qquad 1^3 + 2^3 + 3^3 + 4^3$$
$$1^3 + 2^3 + 3^3 + 4^3 + 5^3$$

15 **18.** A sheet of graph paper is placed with its *x*-axis pointing due east and its *y*-axis pointing due north. A sluggish snail starts at point $(0,0)$ and slowly, but smoothly, slithers 1 unit north, 2 units east, 3 units south, 4 units west, 5 units north, 6 units east, 7 units south, 8 units west, 9 units north and (lastly!) 10 units east.

At which point does the snail finally arrive?

15 **19.** At the first ever *World Worm-Charming Championship*, held at Wollaston, Cheshire in July 1980, Tom Shufflebottom charmed a record 510 worms out of his 3 m × 3 m patch of ground in 30 minutes.

Suppose that each worm has length 20 cm (and they stop wriggling).

When they are laid out end to end, how many times round the perimeter of Tom's patch would the worms stretch?

15 **20.** Donna made a coloured tower as shown.

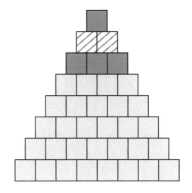

She used thirty-six small cubes in three colours, with equal numbers of red, blue and yellow. Each row is of one colour, and no two rows that are next to each other are the same colour.

The top cube is red, the next row down is blue, and the next row down is red.

What colour is the bottom row?

Part II

More challenging problems

Three dimensions

Exercise 18

4 **1.** The net shown is folded to make a cube.
Which letter is opposite X in the final cube?

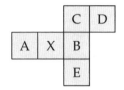

6 **2.** The diagram shows the same cube seen from three different positions.

Which letter is on the face opposite U?

8 **3.** The diagram shows the net of a cube.

Which edge meets the edge X when the net is folded to form the cube?

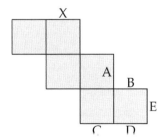

8   **4.** A solid square-based pyramid has all of its corners cut off, as shown.

How many edges does the resulting shape have?

12   **5.** The sculpture '*Cubo Vazado*' [Emptied Cube] by the Brazilian artist Franz Weissmann is formed by removing cubical blocks from a solid cube to leave the symmetrical shape shown. All the edges have length 1, 2 or 3.

What is the volume of the sculpture?

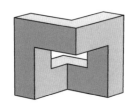

14   **6.** The diagram shows a cuboid in which the area of the hatched face is one quarter of the area of each of the two other visible faces. The total surface area of the cuboid is $72\,\text{cm}^2$.

What is the area of one of the visible unhatched faces of the cuboid, in cm^2?

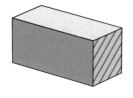

14   **7.** A solid wooden cube is painted blue on the outside. The cube is then cut into eight smaller cubes of equal size.

What fraction of the total surface area of these new cubes is blue?

14   **8.** How many of the following five nets could be folded to make a cube?

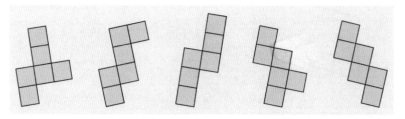

17   **9.** Just William's cousin, Sweet William, has a rectangular block of fudge measuring 2 inches × 3 inches × 6 inches. He wants to cut the block up into cubes whose edge-lengths are whole numbers of inches.

What is the smallest number of cubes he can obtain?

20 **10.** The diagram shows a pyramid made up of 30 cubes, each measuring $1\,m \times 1\,m \times 1\,m$.

What is the total surface area of the whole pyramid (including its base)?

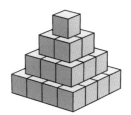

20 **11.** One cube has each of its faces covered by one face of an identical cube, making the solid shown. The volume of the solid is $875\,cm^3$.

What is the surface area of the solid, in cm^2?

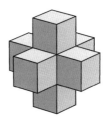

20 **12.** Sally has 72 small wooden cubes, each measuring $1\,cm \times 1\,cm \times 1\,cm$. She arranges them all so that they form a cuboid. The perimeter of the base of the cuboid is $16\,cm$.

What is the height of the cuboid?

20 **13.** Which of the following five cubes could have been made by folding the net on the right?

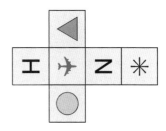

21 **14.** Pablo's teacher has given him 27 identical white cubes. She asks him to paint some of the faces of these cubes grey and then stack the cubes so that they appear as shown.

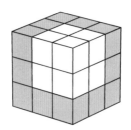

What is the largest possible number of the individual white cubes which Pablo can leave with no faces painted grey?

24 **15.** A $5 \times 5 \times 5$ cube is made by gluing $1 \times 1 \times 1$ cubes together.

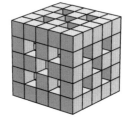

Some of these small cubes are then removed by 'drilling' right through the large cube as shown.

How many of the small cubes remain?

25 **16.** The diagram shows a unit cube coloured blue.

Additional blue unit cubes are glued face-to-face to each of its six faces to form a three-dimensional 'cross'.

Unit cubes coloured yellow are now glued face-to-face to all the spare faces of this cross.

How many yellow unit cubes are required?

25 **17.** A cardboard cube is cut along its edges by a cut following the line shown in the diagram.

The cube is then opened out and placed flat on a table.

Which of the following five nets could result?

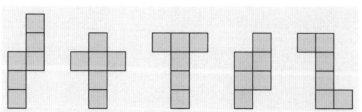

More fractions and percentages

Exercise 19

14 **1.** When the following five fractions are arranged in increasing order of size, which one is in the middle?

$$\frac{1}{2} \qquad \frac{2}{3} \qquad \frac{3}{5} \qquad \frac{4}{7} \qquad \frac{5}{9}$$

14 **2.** Which of the following five fractions has the greatest value?

$$\frac{1+2}{2+3} \qquad \frac{2+4}{2+3} \qquad \frac{1+2}{4+6} \qquad \frac{1+4}{1+3} \qquad \frac{3+4}{2+4}$$

15 **3.** The Grand Old Duke of York had 10 000 men. He lost 10% of them on the way to the top of the hill, and he lost 15% of the rest as he marched them back down the hill.

What percentage of the 10 000 men were still there when they reached the bottom of the hill?

15   **4.** Talulah plants 60 tulip bulbs. When they flower, she notes that half are yellow; one third of those which are not yellow are red; and one quarter of those which are neither yellow nor red are pink. The remainder are white.

What fraction of the tulips are white?

15   **5.** Which of the following five fractions is *not* equal to $\frac{1}{4}$?

$$\frac{3942}{15768} \qquad \frac{4392}{17568} \qquad \frac{5796}{23184} \qquad \frac{6957}{31248} \qquad \frac{7956}{31824}$$

15   **6.** Granny spends one third of her weekly pension on Thursday night, and one quarter of what remains on Friday.

What fraction of the original amount is left for her big night out on Saturday?

15   **7.** In which of the following five lists are the terms *not* increasing?

$$\frac{1}{5}, 0.25, \frac{3}{10}, 0.5 \qquad \frac{3}{5}, 0.7, \frac{4}{5}, 1.5 \qquad \frac{2}{5}, 0.5, \frac{7}{10}, 0.9 \qquad \frac{3}{5}, 0.5, \frac{4}{5}, 0.9$$

$$\frac{2}{5}, 1.5, \frac{10}{5}, 2.3$$

16   **8.** One of the examination papers for Amy's Advanced Arithmetic Award was worth 18% of the final total. The maximum possible mark on this paper was 108 marks.

How many marks were available overall?

16   **9.** The kettle in Keith's kitchen is 80% full. After 20% of the water in it has been poured out, there are 1152 ml of water left.

What volume of water does Keith's kitchen kettle hold when it is full?

17   **10.** There are six more girls than boys in Miss Spelling's class of 24 pupils.

What is the ratio of girls to boys in this class?

17 **11.** In this *multiplication magic square*, the product of the three numbers in each row, each column and each of the two main diagonals is 1.

What is the value of $r + s$?

p	q	r
s	1	t
u	4	$\frac{1}{8}$

18 **12.** Each of the fractions $\dfrac{2637}{18\,459}$ and $\dfrac{5274}{36\,918}$ uses the digits 1 to 9 exactly once.

The first fraction simplifies to $\dfrac{1}{7}$.

What is the simplified form of the second fraction?

18 **13.** Using all of the digits from 1 to 9 inclusive, Shahb wrote down a fraction which had four digits in the numerator and five digits in the denominator.

He then noticed that the fraction simplified to give exactly one half.

Which of the following five integers could have been the numerator of Shahb's fraction?

     5314   6729   7341   7629   8359

19 **14.** Three boxes under my stairs contain apples or pears or both. Each box contains the same number of pieces of fruit. The first box contains all twelve of the apples and one-ninth of the pears.

How many pieces of fruit are there in each box?

19 **15.** A swimming club has three categories of members: junior, senior, veteran. The ratio of junior to senior members is 3 : 2 and the ratio of senior members to veterans is 5 : 2.

Which of the following could be the total number of members in the swimming club?

     30   35   48   58   60

19   **16.**
$$\frac{1}{12} + \frac{1}{24} = \frac{1}{x}.$$

What is the value of x?

19   **17.** The numbers $\frac{1}{2}$, x, y, $\frac{3}{4}$ are in increasing order of size. The differences between successive numbers in this list are all the same.

What is the value of y?

20   **18.** At half-time, Boarwarts Academy had scored all of the points so far in their annual match against Range Hill School. In the second half, each side scored three points. At the end of the match, Boarwarts Academy had scored 90% of the points.

What fraction of the points in the match was scored in the second half?

23   **19.** At a holiday camp, the ratio of boys to girls is 3 : 4 and the ratio of girls to adults is 5 : 7.

What is the ratio of children to adults at the camp?

24   **20.** After playing 500 games, my success rate at Spider Solitaire is 49%.

Assuming I win every game from now on, how many extra games do I need to play in order that my success rate increases to 50%?

Miscellany 3

Exercise 20

16   **1.** Which of the following five diagrams could be the result of repeatedly following the instructions on the right?

Move forward 2 units.
Turn right.
Move forward 15 units.
Turn right.
Move forward 20 units.
Turn right.

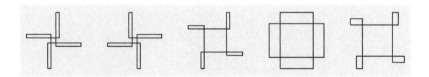

16   **2.** A robot, which is initially facing north, is programmed to travel 5 m then turn through 10°, travel 5 m then turn through 20°, travel 5 m then turn through 30°, and so on. Each move consists of moving 5 m in a straight line and then turning clockwise through an angle which increases by 10° at each move.

How far has the robot travelled by the time it is first facing due east at the *end* of a move?

16   **3.** A book has 256 pages with, on average, 33 lines on each page and 9 words on each line.

To the nearest five thousand, how many words are in the book?

16   **4.** I have some strange dice; the faces show the numbers 1 to 6 as usual, except that the odd numbers are negative, that is, each die has −1, −3 and −5 in place of 1, 3 and 5.

When I throw two such dice, which of the following five totals *cannot* be achieved?

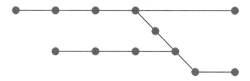

| 3 | 4 | 5 | 7 | 8 |

17   **5.** The diagram is a 'map' of Jo's local rail network, where the dots represent stations and the lines are routes.

Jo wants to visit all the stations, travelling only by train, starting at any station and ending at any station, with no restrictions on which routes are taken.

What is the smallest number of stations that Jo has to go to more than once?

17 **6.** The tiling pattern shown uses two sizes of square, with sides of length 1 and 4.

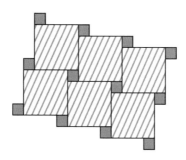

A very large number of these squares is used to tile an enormous floor in this pattern.

Which of the following five ratios is closest to the ratio of the number of grey tiles on the floor to the number of hatched tiles?

$$1:1 \qquad 4:3 \qquad 3:2 \qquad 2:1 \qquad 4:1$$

17 **7.** In how many different ways can a row of five 'on-off' switches be set so that no two adjacent switches are in the 'off' position?

17 **8.** The diagram shows rectangle *PRSU* and straight line *QT*, which divides the rectangle into two squares.

How many right-angled triangles can be drawn using any three of the points *P, Q, R, S, T, U* as corners?

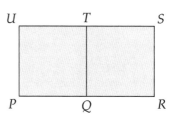

17 **9.** Exactly one of the following five statements is correct. Which one?

$$44^2 + 77^2 = 4477 \qquad 55^2 + 66^2 = 5566 \qquad 66^2 + 55^2 = 6655$$
$$88^2 + 33^2 = 8833 \qquad 99^2 + 22^2 = 9922$$

17 **10.** 5p, 2p and 1p coins (or a mixture of any or all of these) are used to make a total of 11p.

In how many different ways can this be done?

18 **11.** Which of the following five statements is correct?

$$15\,614 = 1 + 5^6 - 1 \times 4 \qquad 15\,615 = 1 + 5^6 - 1 \times 5$$
$$15\,616 = 1 + 5^6 - 1 \times 6 \qquad 15\,617 = 1 + 5^6 - 1 \times 7$$
$$15\,618 = 1 + 5^6 - 1 \times 8$$

18 **12.** The UKMT logo depicts a single strip of paper with 'UKMT' in the positions X, Y and Z.

Which of these are written on the same side of the paper?

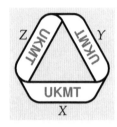

X and Y	Y and Z	X and Z
X, Y and Z	none of them	

18 **13.** A circle is added to the grid of dots in the diagram alongside.

What is the largest number of dots that the circle can pass through?

19 **14.** One of the following five cubes is the smallest cube that can be written as the sum of three positive cubes. Which is it?

$$27 \qquad 64 \qquad 125 \qquad 216 \qquad 512$$

19 **15.** Pat wants to travel down every one of the roads shown at least once, starting and finishing at home.

What is the smallest number of the five villages that Pat will have to visit more than once?

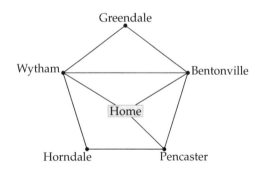

19 **16.** Pinocchio's nose is 5 cm long. Each time he tells a lie his nose doubles in length.

After he has told nine lies, which of the following has roughly the same length as Pinocchio's nose?

> a domino a tennis racquet a snooker table
> a tennis court a football pitch

19 **17.** A newspaper has thirty-six pages.

Which three other pages are on the same sheet as page 10?

20 **18.** In the diagram on the right, the number in each box is obtained by adding the numbers in the two boxes immediately underneath.

What is the value of x?

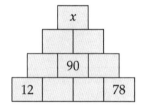

20 **19.** Five children Z, A, B, C, and D are playing a game using a set of ten cards numbered from 1 to 10. They are each dealt two cards with the following five totals.

$$Z = 4$$
$$A = 11$$
$$B = 12$$
$$C = 13$$
$$D = 15$$

Is it possible to tell who has the card numbered 9? If so, who?

Placement

Exercise 21

13   **1.** The diagram shows five circles placed at the corners of a pentagon. The numbers 1, 2, 3, 4, 5 are placed in the circles shown, one in each, so that the numbers in adjacent circles always differ by more than 1.

     What is the sum of the numbers in the two circles adjacent to the circle which contains the number 5?

13   **2.** The diagram shows a 3×3 grid. One of the numbers 1, 2 and 3 is to be entered in each of the nine cells so that each row and each column contains one 1, one 2 and one 3 in some order.

     In the completed grid, what is the value of $M + N$?

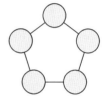

17   **3.** Four crosses are to be placed in this 4×4 grid so that no two crosses go in the same row or column, or in any of the ten 'diagonals'.

     The position of the first cross is given.

     When the grid has been completed, which cell in the third column will contain a cross?

18 **4.** The numbers 2, 3, 4, 5, 6, 7, 8 are to be placed, one per cell, in the diagram shown so that the four numbers in the row across add up to 21 and the four numbers in the column down also add up to 21.

Which number should replace x?

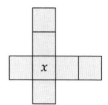

18 **5.** In this magic square, which uses all the integers from 7 to 15 inclusive, each of the rows, columns and the two main diagonals has the same total.

Which number replaces n in the completed square?

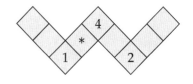

20 **6.** The integers from 1 to 9 inclusive are to be placed, one number to a cell, in the figure shown, so that the total of the three numbers in each of the four lines is the same.

What number should replace $*$?

21 **7.** The grid is completed with the letters A, B, C, D and E so that no row, column or either of the two main diagonal lines contains the same letter more than once.

Which letter should replace the asterisk?

23 **8.** Sam wants to complete the diagram so that each of the nine circles contains one of the digits from 1 to 9 inclusive and each contains a different digit.

Also, the digits in each of the three lines of four circles are to have the same total.

What is this total?

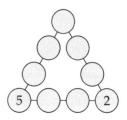

25   **9.** In a magic square each row, each column and both main diagonals have the same total.

What number should replace x in this partially completed magic square?

13		
5		15
x		

More time and dates

Exercise 22

16   1. Ulysses, Kim, Mei and Tanika had their 12th, 14th, 15th and 15th birthdays on the same day in 2013.

In what year will their ages first total 100?

16   2. Humpty Dumpty sat on a wall, admiring his new digital watch which displayed hours and minutes only.

He noticed that his watch showed 15:21 when Jack and Jill set off up the hill, but that when they later came tumbling down again his watch showed only 10:51. At that point Humpty realised that he had been wearing his watch upside down all the time!

How long did Jack and Jill take to go up the hill and down again?

17   3. The match in 2010 at Wimbledon between John Isner and Nicolas Mahut, which lasted 11 hours and 5 minutes, set a record for the longest match in tennis history. The fifth set of the match lasted 8 hours and 11 minutes.

Which of the following five fractions is approximately the fraction of the whole match that was taken up by the fifth set?

$$\frac{1}{5} \qquad \frac{2}{5} \qquad \frac{3}{5} \qquad \frac{3}{4} \qquad \frac{9}{10}$$

18 **4.** Peri the winkle leaves on Monday to go and visit Granny, 90 m away. Except for rest days, Peri travels 1 m each day (24-hour period) at a constant rate and without pause. However, Peri stops for a 24-hour rest every tenth day, that is, after every nine days' travelling.

On which day of the week does Peri arrive at Granny's?

20 **5.** Aroon says his age is 50 years, 50 months, 50 weeks and 50 days.

How many years old will he be on his next birthday?

21 **6.** Tick's watch runs 2 minutes per hour too slow. Tock's watch runs 1 minute per hour too fast. They set them to the same time at noon on Sunday.

The next time they met, one of the watches was one hour ahead of the other.

What was the earliest time this could have been?

21 **7.** Granny says "I am 84 years old—not counting my Sundays".

How old is she really?

22 **8.** On a digital clock displaying hours, minutes and seconds, how many times in each 24-hour period do all six digits change simultaneously?

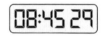

22 **9.** How many times between midday and midnight is the hour hand of a normal 12-hour clock at right angles to the minute hand?

22 **10.** The Grand Old Duke of York, he had ten thousand men, he marched them up to the top of the hill, ...

At 2 pm they were one-third of the way up. At 4 pm they were three-quarters of the way up.

At what time did they set out?

25   **11.** Last year Gill took a multiple-choice test, which had 25 questions and lasted for one hour.

(i) Five marks were awarded for each correct answer to questions 1–15.

(ii) Six marks were awarded for each correct answer to questions 16–25.

(iii) One mark was deducted for each incorrect answer to questions 16–20.

(iv) Two marks were deducted for each incorrect answer to questions 21–25.

Gill answered all the questions she did correctly. The first question took her 1 second, question two took her 2 seconds, question three took her 4 seconds, and so on, the time doubling for each question. What was Gill's score?

More angles

Exercise 23

16 **1.** The diagram shows a square inside an equilateral triangle.

What is the value of $x + y$?

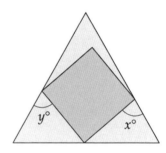

16 **2.** What is the sum of the six marked angles?

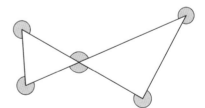

17   **3.** What is the value of x?

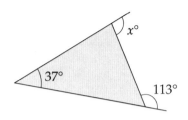

18   **4.** Triangle PQR is equilateral.
     Angle SPR is 40° and angle
     TQR is 35°.
     What is the value of x?

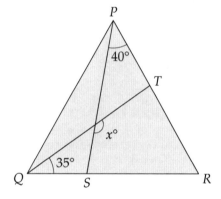

18   **5.** The three angles of a triangle are $(x + 10)°$, $(2x - 40)°$ and $(3x - 90)°$.
     Which of the following five phrases could correctly be used to describe
     the triangle?

>   right-angled isosceles   right-angled, but not isosceles
>   equilateral   obtuse-angled and isosceles   scalene

19   **6.** In rectangle $PQRS$, the ratio of angle QSP to angle PQS is 1 : 5.
     What is the size of angle RSQ?

19 **7.** The diagram shows a rhombus *FGHI* and an isosceles triangle *FGJ* in which *FG* = *GJ*. Angle *FJI* is equal to 111°.

What is the size of angle *IFJ*?

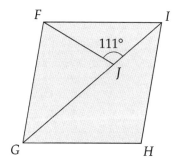

19 **8.** In the diagram, *TP* = *TQ* = *TS*, *QS* = *SR*, and angle *PQT* = 20°.

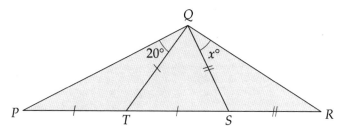

What is the value of *x*?

20 **9.** The diagram shows a regular pentagon *PQRST* and a regular hexagon *PRUVWX*.

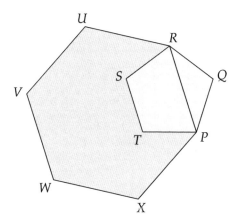

What is the size of angle *SRU*?

21   **10.** In the diagram, $CA = AB$ and $z < 90$.

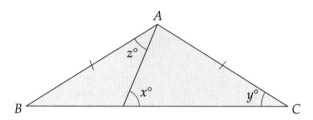

What is the value of z in terms of x and y?

23   **11.** The points S, T and U lie on the sides of the triangle PQR so that $UQ = QS$, $SR = RT$ and angle $UST = 40°$, as shown.

What is the size of angle TPU?

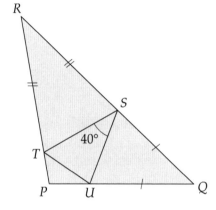

23   **12.** In the diagram, triangle XYZ is isosceles, with $ZX = XY$.

What is the value of r in terms of p and q?

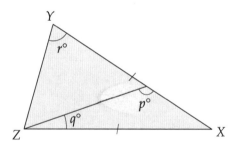

23 **13.** In the diagram, $CA = AB$ and $AD = DC$.

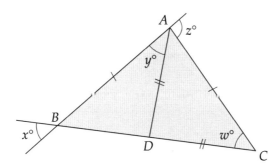

Referring to the labelled angles, how many of the following three statements are correct, whatever the values of x, y, z and w?

$$w = x \qquad x + y + z = 180 \qquad z = 2x$$

25 **14.** The four straight lines in the diagram are such that $UV = VW$.

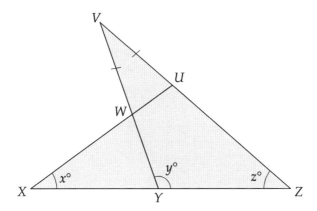

The sizes of angles UXZ, VYZ and XZV are $x°$, $y°$ and $z°$.

What is the value of x in terms of y and z?

25 **15.** The interior angles of a triangle are $5m° + 3n°$, $3m° + 20°$ and $10n° + 30°$, where m and n are positive integers.

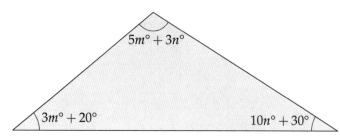

What is the value of $m + n$?

More algebra

Exercise 24

16 **1.** Five pings and five pongs are worth the same as two pongs and eleven pings.

How many pings is a pong worth?

17 **2.** In a group of 48 children, the ratio of boys to girls is 3 : 5.

How many boys need to join the group to make the ratio of boys to girls 5 : 3?

17 **3.** The lengths of the sides of the equilateral triangle PQR are as shown.

Which of the following could *not* be the value of (x, y)?

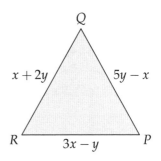

$(18, 12)$	$(15, 10)$	$(12, 8)$
$(10, 6)$	$(3, 2)$	

17 **4.** A rectangle is formed by doubling both the length and the width of the rectangle shown in the diagram.

What is the area of this new rectangle in terms of a?

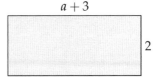

18   **5.** Weighing the baby at the clinic was a problem. The baby would not keep still and caused the scales to wobble.

So I held the baby and stood on the scales while the nurse read off 78 kg. Then the nurse held the baby while I read off 69 kg. Finally I held the nurse while the baby read off 137 kg.

What was the combined weight of all three of us?

18   **6.** Granny swears that she is getting younger.

She has calculated that she is four times as old as I am now, but remembers that 5 years ago she was five times as old as I was at that time.

What is the sum of our ages now?

19   **7.** The values of a, b and c are all positive, and $a \times b = 2$, $b \times c = 24$ and $c \times a = 3$.

What is the value of $a + b + c$?

19   **8.** When the diagram is complete, the number in the middle of each group of three adjoining cells is the average of its two neighbours.

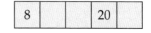

What number goes in the right-hand end cell?

19   **9.** The number of diagonals of a certain regular polygon is equal to twice the number of sides.

How many sides has the polygon?

20 **10.** In the seventh century, the Indian mathematician Brahmagupta gave the following formula for the area A of a cyclic quadrilateral whose sides have lengths a, b, c, d:

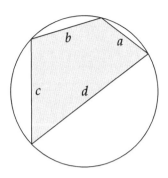

$$A = \sqrt{(s - a)(s - b)(s - c)(s - d)},$$

where s is half of the perimeter length of the quadrilateral.

What is the area of a cyclic quadrilateral with sides of length 4, 5, 7 and 10?

[*A cyclic quadrilateral has all four vertices on the circumference of a circle.*]

20 **11.** Despite his name, Mr Bean likes to eat lots of fruit. He finds that four apples and two oranges cost £1.54 and that two oranges and four bananas cost £1.70.

How much would he have to pay if he bought one apple, one orange and one banana?

21 **12.** The totals of the entries in the rows and columns are as shown.

What is the value of ♥?

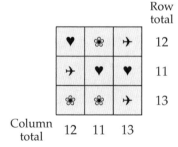

22 **13.** Two builders, Bob and Geri, buy bricks at the same price. Bob sells 10 for £6 and Geri sells 12 for £7.

When Bob has gained £4 more than Geri, they have sold equal numbers of bricks.

How many bricks has each sold?

22 **14.** Four identical blocks of wood are placed touching a table in the positions shown in this view from the side.

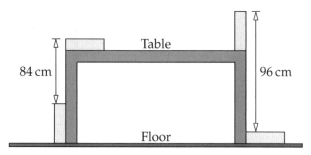

How high is the table?

23 **15.** The currency used on the planet Zog consists of bank notes of a fixed size differing only in colour.

> Three green notes and eight blue notes are worth 46 zogs;
> eight green notes and three blue notes are worth 31 zogs.

How many zogs are two green notes and three blue notes worth?

23 **16.** The diagram shows a square with sides of length y divided into a square with sides of length x and four congruent rectangles.

What is the length of the longer side of each rectangle in terms of x and y?

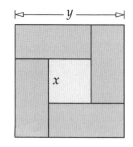

24 **17.** Amrita has written down four numbers. When she chooses three of her numbers at a time and adds up each triple, she obtains totals of 115, 153, 169 and 181.

What is the largest of Amrita's numbers?

18. Five identical rectangles fit together as shown.

What is the total area that they cover?

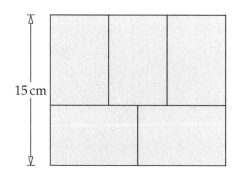

15 cm

19. In a sequence of positive integers, every term after the first two terms is the sum of the two previous terms in the sequence. The fifth term is 2004.

What is the maximum possible value of the first term?

More reasoning

Exercise 25

16   **1.** Only one of the following five statements is true. Which one?

> The second statement is true.
> The fifth statement is false.
> All five statements are true.
> All five statements are false.
> The first statement is false.

16   **2.** Beth, Carolyn and George love reading their favourite bedtime story together. They take it in turns to read a page, always in the order Beth, then Carolyn, then George. All twenty pages of the story are read on each occasion.

One evening, Beth is staying at Grandma's house but Carolyn and George still read the same bedtime story and take it in turns to read a page with Carolyn reading the first page.

In total, how many pages are read by the person who usually reads that page?

16   **3.** My bus fare is 44p. The driver can give me change.

What is the smallest number of coins which can change hands when I pay this fare?

17 **4.**

> Knave of Hearts: "I stole the tarts."
>
> Knave of Clubs: "The Knave of Hearts is lying."
>
> Knave of Diamonds: "The Knave of Clubs is lying."
>
> Knave of Spades: "The Knave of Diamonds is lying."

How many of the four Knaves were telling the truth?

19 **5.** Jack and Jill played a game for two people. In each game, the winner was awarded 2 points and the loser 1 point. No games were drawn. Jack won exactly 4 games and Jill had a final score of 10 points.

How many games did they play?

20 **6.** Box P has p chocolates and box Q has q chocolates, where p and q are both odd and $p > q$.

In terms of p and q, what is the smallest number of chocolates which would have to be moved from box P to box Q so that box Q has more chocolates than box P?

20 **7.** How many of the statements in the box are true?

> None of these statements is true.
>
> Exactly one of these statements is true.
>
> Exactly two of these statements are true.
>
> All of these statements are true.

21 **8.** The 5×4 grid is divided into blocks. Each block is a square or a rectangle and contains the number of cells indicated by the integer within it.

Which integer will be in the same block as the shaded cell?

21 **9.**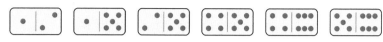

Dominic wants to place the six dominoes above in a hexagonal ring so that, for every pair of adjacent dominoes, the numbers of pips match.

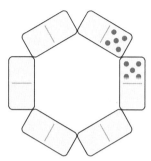

The ring shown alongside indicates how one adjacent pair match.

In a completed ring, how many of the other five dominoes can he definitely not place adjacent to ?

21 **10.** A list of ten numbers contains two of each of the numbers 0, 1, 2, 3 and 4. The two 0s are next to each other, the two 1s are separated by one number, the two 2s by two numbers, the two 3s by three numbers and the two 4s by four numbers.

The list starts 3, 4.

What is the last number?

23 **11.** A single polygon is made by joining dots in the grid with straight lines, which meet only at dots at their end points. No dot is at more than one corner.

The diagram shows a polygon with five sides formed in this way.

What is the greatest possible number of edges of a polygon formed by joining the dots using these same rules?

23 **12.** Granny tells Dilly that her glove drawer contains 1 left-hand blue glove, 2 left-hand green gloves, 3 right-hand blue gloves, and 4 right-hand green gloves, and asks her to bring a pair of gloves from the drawer. Unfortunately Dilly cannot tell the difference between left-hand and right-hand gloves, but, thankfully, can identify blue and green.

What is the smallest number of gloves that Dilly should bring, in order to be sure that these include a matching pair?

24 **13.** Two adults and two children wish to cross a river. They make a raft but it will carry only the weight of one adult or two children. The raft cannot cross the river without at least one person on board.

What is the minimum number of times the raft needs to cross the river to get all four people to the other side?

24 **14.** Boris, Spike and Percival are going to race up the 99 steps that lead from the beach to the car park at the top of the cliff.

Boris can run up five steps in the same time as Spike can run up four steps, which is the same time as Percival can run up three steps.

It is agreed that Boris starts from the bottom, Spike starts 21 steps up and Percival 38 steps up. They all start at the same time.

In what order will they reach the top?

25 **15.** Seven towns P, Q, R, S, T, U and V lie (in that order) along a road. The table shown is meant to give all the distances between pairs of towns. For example, the distance from P to S is 23 km.

Unfortunately, several of the distances are missing.

How many of the missing distances can be calculated from the given information?

P						
	Q					
		R				
23			S			
	30			T		
58		40			U	
	68		53			V

More areas and perimeters

Exercise 26

16 **1.** The diagram shows an equilateral triangle with its corners at the midpoints of alternate sides of a regular hexagon.

What fraction of the area of the hexagon is shaded?

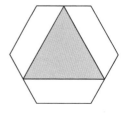

17 **2.** A 5 cm × 5 cm square is cut into five pieces, as shown.

Each cut is a sequence of identical copies of the same shape but pointing up, down, left or right.

Which piece has the longest perimeter?

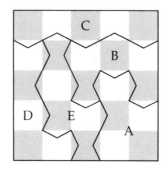

18   **3.** A shape consisting of 2004 small squares is made by continuing the pattern shown in the diagram. The small squares have sides of length 1 cm.

How many centimetres long is the perimeter of the whole shape?

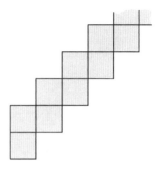

18   **4.** A right-angled triangle has the dimensions shown.

What is the area of the shaded region?

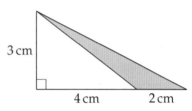

19   **5.** The points *P, Q, R* and *S* lie in that order along a straight line, with *PQ* = *QR* = *RS* = 2 cm. Semicircular arcs with diameters *PQ, QR, RS* and *SP* are joined to make the shape shown on the right.

What is the area of the shape?

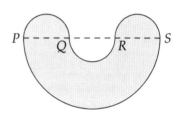

19   **6.** Two identical rectangular cards are glued together as shown to form an L-shape. The perimeter of this L-shape has length 40 cm.

What is the length of the longer side of one of the original cards?

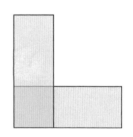

19   **7.** What fraction of the large rectangle is shaded?

20 **8.** The diagram shows a rectangular wire grid which forms twelve small squares. The length of the grid is *a*.

What is the total length of wire required to make the grid?

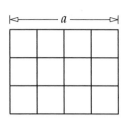

21 **9.** The diagram shows a pentagon drawn on a square grid. All vertices of the pentagon and triangle are grid points.

What fraction of the area of the pentagon is shaded?

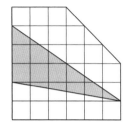

21 **10.** A shape consisting of a number of regular hexagons is made by continuing to the right the pattern shown in the diagram, with each extra hexagon sharing one side with the preceding one.

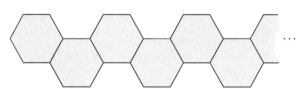

Each hexagon has sides of length 1 cm.

How many hexagons are required for the perimeter of the whole shape to have length 2010 cm?

22 **11.** Four copies of the triangle shown are joined together, without gaps or overlaps, to make a parallelogram.

What is the largest possible length of the perimeter of the parallelogram?

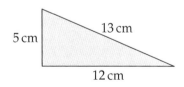

22 **12.** The diagram shows a shaded region inside a regular hexagon. The shaded region is divided into equilateral triangles.

What fraction of the area of the hexagon is shaded?

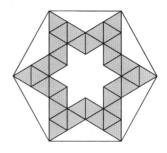

22 **13.** The diagram shows a design formed by drawing six lines in a regular hexagon. The lines divide each side of the hexagon into three equal parts.

What fraction of the hexagon is shaded?

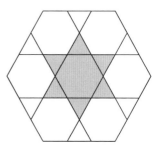

23 **14.** The diagram shows four shaded glass squares, with areas $1\,cm^2$, $4\,cm^2$, $9\,cm^2$ and $16\,cm^2$, placed in the corners of a rectangle.

The largest square overlaps two others.

The area of the region inside the rectangle but not covered by any square (shown unshaded) is $1.5\,cm^2$.

What is the area of the region where the squares overlap (shown in dark grey)?

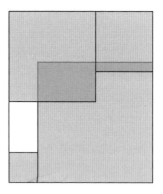

24 **15.** The diagram shows a regular octagon with sides of length 1. The octagon is divided into regions by four diagonals.

What is the difference between the area of the crosshatched region and the area of the region shaded grey?

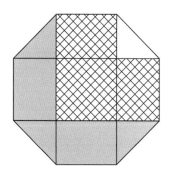

24 **16.** Three congruent squares overlap as shown.

The areas of the three overlapping regions are $2\,cm^2$, $5\,cm^2$ and $8\,cm^2$ respectively. The total area of the non-overlapping parts of the squares is $117\,cm^2$.

What is the side-length of each square?

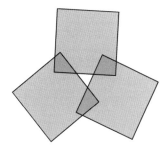

24 **17.** The parallelogram $WXYZ$ in the diagram has been divided into nine smaller parallelograms.

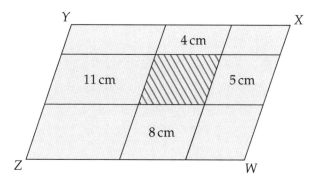

The lengths of the perimeters of four of the smaller parallelograms are shown. The length of the perimeter of $WXYZ$ is 21 cm.

What is the perimeter length of the hatched parallelogram?

25 **18.** The diagram shows four overlapping squares which have sides of
length 5 cm, 7 cm, 9 cm and 11 cm.

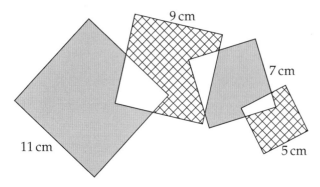

What is the difference between the total area shaded grey and the total
crosshatched area?

More integers

Exercise 27

16   **1.** The pupils in Year 8 are holding a mock election. A candidate receiving more votes than any other wins. The four candidates receive 83 votes between them.

What is the smallest number of votes the winner could receive?

16   **2.** 'Saturn' chocolate bars are packed either in boxes of 5 or boxes of 12.

What is the smallest number of full boxes required to pack exactly 2005 'Saturn' bars?

17   **3.** Lollipops cost 12p each, but I get 3 for 30p. I have £2 to spend.

What is the maximum number of lollipops I can buy?

18   **4.** Sam's 101st birthday is tomorrow. So Sam's age in years changes from a square (100) to a prime (101).

How many times has this happened before in Sam's lifetime?

18   **5.** Six friends are having dinner together in their local restaurant.

> The first eats there every day;
> the second eats there every other day;
> the third eats there every third day;
> the fourth eats there every fourth day;
> the fifth eats there every fifth day; and
> the sixth eats there every sixth day.

They agree to have a party the next time they all eat together there.
In how many days is the party?

19   **6.** A list is made of every digit that is the units digit of at least one prime number.

How many of the following five numbers appear in the list?

> 1   2   3   4   5

20   **7.** Nicky has to choose seven different positive integers whose average is 7.

What is the largest possible such number she could choose?

20   **8.** The sum of three different prime numbers is 40.

What is the difference between the two biggest of these three numbers?

21   **9.** Tickets for a school play cost £3 for adults and £1 for children.

The total amount collected from ticket sales was £1320. The play was staged in a hall seating 600, but the hall was not completely full.

What is the smallest possible number of adult tickets sold?

22   **10.** Last week Evariste and Sophie both bought some stamps for their collections. Each stamp Evariste bought cost him £1.10, whilst Sophie paid 70p for each of her stamps. Between them they spent exactly £10.

How many stamps did they buy in total?

22   **11.** Kiran writes down six different prime numbers p, q, r, s, t and u, all less than 20, such that $p + q = r + s = t + u$.

What is the value of $p + q$?

22 **12.** Only one choice of the digit d gives a prime number for each of the three-digit numbers read across and downwards in the diagram on the right.

Which digit is d?

		5	
1	d	3
		7	

22 **13.** A positive integer less than 100 has remainder 2 when it is divided by 3, remainder 3 when it is divided by 4 and remainder 4 when it is divided by 5.

What is its remainder when it is divided by 7?

22 **14.** When 26 is divided by the positive integer N, the remainder is 2.

What is the sum of all the possible values of N?

23 **15.** In our school netball league a team gains a certain whole number of points when it wins a game, a lower positive whole number of points when it draws a game and no points when it loses a game.

After 10 games my team has won 7 games, drawn 3 and gained 44 points. My sister's team has won 5 games, drawn 2 and lost 3.

How many points has my sister's team gained?

23 **16.** Peter wrote a list of all the numbers that can be produced by changing one digit of the number 200.

How many of the numbers on Peter's list are prime?

23 **17.** A certain positive integer has exactly eight divisors including 1 and itself. Two of its divisors are 21 and 35.

What is the integer?

24 **18.** What is the difference between the largest and smallest five-digit palindromic numbers that are both multiples of 45?

[A palindromic number is a positive integer that reads the same when the order of its digits is reversed.]

24 **19.** The following box contains a list of integers from 11 to 19, so that each successive pair (such as 12 and 14, or 18 and 15) has highest common factor greater than 1.

| 16 | 18 | 15 | 12 | 14 |

When the longest possible list like this is made, but using integers from 111 to 119, how many integers from 111 to 119 are left out?

25 **20.** In Miss Quaffley's class, one third of the pupils bring a teddy bear to school.

Last term, each boy took 12 books out of the library, each girl took 17 books and each teddy bear took 9 books. In total, 305 books were taken out.

How many girls are there in Miss Quaffley's class?

More digits

Exercise 28

16 **1.** In this multiplication each letter represents a different digit.

Which letter represents 3?

$$\begin{array}{r} A\ 6\ B\ C \\ \times\ 7 \\ \hline D\ 9\ E\ 9\ 8 \end{array}$$

17 **2.** The first and third digits of the five-digit number '$d6d41$' are the same. The number is a multiple of nine.

What is the value of the digit d?

17 **3.** The eight-digit number '$1234d678$' is a multiple of eleven.

What is the value of the digit d?

18 **4.** In the addition shown, each letter represents a different non-zero digit.

What digit does X represent?

$$\begin{array}{r} S\ E\ E \\ +\ S\ E\ E \\ \hline A\ X\ E\ S \end{array}$$

18 **5.** The letters J, M, C represent three different non-zero digits.

What is the value of $J + M + C$?

$$\begin{array}{r} J\ J \\ M\ M \\ +\ C\ C \\ \hline J\ M\ C \end{array}$$

18   **6.** In the subtraction sum alongside, a, b and c are digits, and
      a is less than b.

      What is the value of c?

$$\begin{array}{r} b\,a \\ -\,a\,b \\ \hline c\,6 \end{array}$$

20   **7.** All the integers from 1 to 1000 inclusive are written down.

      Which digit appears the smallest number of times?

20   **8.** A four-digit number, exactly divisible by three, by four, and by five,
      was written on a piece of paper.

      The last two digits were then covered up, as shown.

      What is the sum of the two missing digits?

22   **9.** In the division calculation $952\,473 \div 18$, which two adjacent digits
      should be swapped in order to increase the result by 100?

22   **10.** The digits in the product $13 \times 2 = 26$ can be rearranged to give
      $16 \times 2 = 32$ as well as $31 \times 2 = 62$.

      In which one of the following five statements can the digits *not* be
      rearranged to give another correct product?

$$12 \times 3 = 36 \qquad 12 \times 7 = 84 \qquad 26 \times 3 = 78 \qquad 16 \times 3 = 48$$
$$39 \times 2 = 78.$$

22   **11.** Teams from two schools contest a swimming match. Each school
      enters two swimmers for each event, with 5 points awarded for first
      place, 3 points for second place, 2 points for third place, and 1 point
      for fourth place.

      After six events no swimmer has been disqualified and the leading
      school's score is the reverse of the other school's score.

      What is the difference between their two scores at this stage?

23   **12.** In a 7-digit numerical code each group of four adjacent digits adds to
      16 and each group of five adjacent digits adds to 19.

      What is the sum of all seven digits?

23 **13.** In this addition each letter represents a different digit, with S representing 3.

What is the value of $Y \times O$?

$$\begin{array}{r} S\ O \\ +\ M\ A\ N\ Y \\ \hline S\ U\ M\ S \end{array}$$

24 **14.** The pages of a book are numbered 1, 2, 3, ... In total, it takes 852 digits to number all the pages of the book.

What is the number of the last page?

24 **15.** Gill has recently moved to a new house, which has a three-digit number. The sum of this number and its three individual digits is 429.

What is the product of the three digits that make up the house number?

24 **16.** In the multiplication shown, each letter represents a different digit and only the digits 1, 2, 3, 4 and 5 are used.

Which of the letters represents 2?

$$\begin{array}{r} A\ B \\ \times\ C \\ \hline D\ E \end{array}$$

25 **17.** What is the value of $P + Q + R$ in the multiplication on the right?

$$\begin{array}{r} P\ Q\ P\ Q \\ \times\ R\ R\ R \\ \hline 6\ 3\ 9\ 0\ 2\ 7 \end{array}$$

25 **18.** For how many positive values of n are both $\frac{1}{2}n$ and $2n$ three-digit integers?

25 **19.** The two-digit by two-digit multiplication alongside has lots of gaps, but most of them can be filled in by logical reasoning.

Which digit goes in position $*$?

$$\begin{array}{r} 4\ \_ \\ \times\ \_\ \_ \\ \hline \_\ 8\ \_ \\ 8\ \_\ 0 \\ \hline \_\ \_\ 4\ * \end{array}$$

More spatial problems

Exercise 29

16   **1.** Each of the nine cells in this grid can be coloured completely black or completely white.

What is the largest number of cells that can be coloured black so that the design created has rotational symmetry of order 2, but no lines of symmetry?

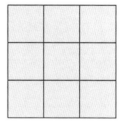

16   **2.** The diagram shows a poster which Beatrix has (this way up!) on her wall.

When Beatrix was standing on her head, looking in a mirror on the opposite wall at the poster on the wall behind her, how many letters could still be read in the normal way?

18   **3.** A square piece of paper measuring 16 ×
     16 is folded in half twice.

     Then pieces are removed by cutting
     through all the resulting layers, leaving
     the shape shown.

     When the paper is unfolded, how many
     square holes are in it?

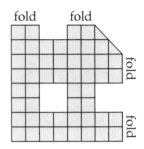

19   **4.** A sheet of A4 paper (297 mm × 210 mm) is folded once, and placed
     flat on a table.

     How many of the following three shapes could be made?

20   **5.** A 'long knight' moves on a square
     grid.

     A single move, such as those shown,
     consists of moving three cells in one
     direction (left, right, up, or down) and
     then one cell at right angles to the first
     direction.

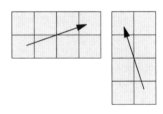

     What is the smallest number of moves a long knight requires to go
     from one corner of an 8 × 8 square board to the diagonally opposite
     corner?

21 **6.** A rectangular sheet of paper is divided into two pieces by a single straight cut. One of the pieces is then further divided into two, also by a single straight cut.

Which of the following could *not* be the total number of edges of the resulting three pieces?

9   10   11   12   13

21 **7.** Which one of the following five shapes could not appear as the overlapping region of two identical squares?

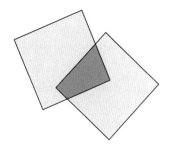

equilateral triangle   square
kite   heptagon
regular octagon

21 **8.** Four of the following five jigsaw pieces fit together to form a square. Which one is not used?

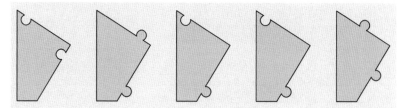

21 **9.** The board for the game *Rorrim* is shown. The aim of the game is to move a counter from the starting square *S* to the target square *T*.

On each move, the counter is moved to the square that is the reflection of its present square in one of the lines of the board.

What is the smallest number of moves required to reach square *T* from square *S*?

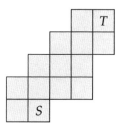

22 **10.** A rectangular piece of card measuring 24 cm × 30 cm is cut into two equal pieces which can be reassembled to form another rectangle measuring 40 cm × 18 cm.

Which of the following five diagrams could show the original rectangle and the cut?

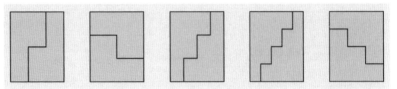

23 **11.** The diagram alongside shows a circle with circumference 1 being rolled around an equilateral triangle with sides of length 1.

How many complete turns does the circle make as it rolls once around the triangle without slipping?

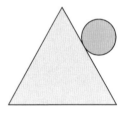

23 **12.** The aim of the game illustrated here is to move a counter from the starting triangle *S* to the target triangle *T*.

On each move, the counter is moved to a triangle on the board that is the reflection of its present triangle in one of the lines of the board.

What is the smallest number of moves required to reach triangle *T* from triangle *S*?

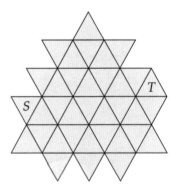

23 **13.** A square is cut into three pieces as shown.

Which of the following five shapes cannot be made by assembling all three pieces without gaps or overlaps?

> quadrilateral   pentagon   hexagon
> heptagon   octagon

25 **14.** Beatrix places dominoes on a 5 × 5 board so that each domino covers two cells. She stops when she cannot place another domino, as in the example shown in the diagram.

When Beatrix stops, what is the largest possible number of cells that may be still uncovered?

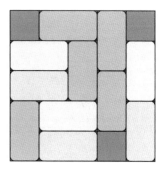

25 **15.** A die has the shape of a regular tetrahedron, with the four faces having 1, 2, 3 and 4 pips.

The die is placed with 4 pips 'face down' in one corner of the triangular grid shown, so that the face with 4 pips precisely covers the triangle marked with 4 pips.

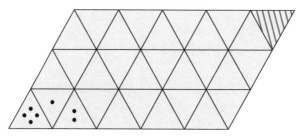

The die is now 'rolled', by rotating about an edge without slipping, so that 1 pip is face down. It is rolled again, so that 2 pips are face down, as indicated. The rolling continues until the die rests on the hatched triangle in the opposite corner of the grid.

How many pips are now face down?

25 **16.** The diagram shows a trapezium made from three equilateral triangles.

Three copies of the trapezium are placed together, without gaps or overlaps and so that only complete sides coincide, to form a polygon with N edges.

How many different values of N are possible?

25 **17.** A piece of paper in the shape of a polygon is folded in half along a line of symmetry. The resulting shape is also folded in half, again along a line of symmetry. The final shape is a triangle.

How many possibilities are there for the number of edges of the original polygon?

Miscellany 4

Exercise 30

21 **1.** Gill is now 27 and has moved into a new flat. She has four pictures to hang in a horizontal row on a wall which is 4800 mm wide. The pictures are identical in size and are 420 mm wide. Gill hangs the first two pictures so that one is on the extreme left of the wall and one is on the extreme right of the wall. She wants to hang the remaining two pictures so that all four pictures are equally spaced.

How far should Gill place the centre of each of the two remaining pictures from a vertical line down the centre of the wall?

21 **2.** Gill leaves Lille by train at 09:00. The train travels the first 27 km at 96 km/h. It then stops at Lens for 3 minutes before travelling the final 29 km to Lillers at 96 km/h.

At what time does Gill arrive at Lillers?

21 **3.** What is the value of $2^8 \div 8^2$?

21 **4.** In a code the vowels A–U in alphabetical order are replaced by the numbers 1–5, while the consonants B–Z in alphabetical order are replaced by the numbers 1–21.

Thus, for example, BABE becomes 1112, and so does ABAC.

The following five words are encoded, and the code numbers for the letters in each word are added up.

MATHS   EQUALS   ALGEBRA   PLUS   GEOMETRY

Which word has the largest total?

22 **5.** Two numbers in the 4 × 4 grid can be swapped to create a magic square (in which all rows, all columns and both main diagonals add to the same total).

What is the sum of these two numbers?

7	12	15	2
14	1	8	11
4	13	10	5
9	6	3	16

22 **6.** Starting at the cell containing the 2, you are allowed to move from one cell to the next either across a common side, or diagonally through a common corner.

How many different routes are there passing through exactly two cells containing a 0 and ending in one of the cells containing a 9?

2	0	0	9
0	0	0	9
0	0	0	9
9	9	9	9

22 **7.** In a certain code, A = 1, B = 2, C = 3, and so on. Words are encoded by multiplying together the values of their letters, so the code for SQUARE is $19 \times 17 \times 21 \times 1 \times 18 \times 5 = 610\,470$. Similarly, the code for RECTANGLE is $31\,752\,000$.

What is the code for TRIANGLE?

23 **8.** The diagram shows the first few squares of a 'spiral' sequence of squares. All but the first three squares have been labelled.

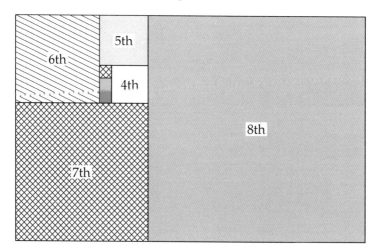

After the first six squares, the sequence is continued by placing the next square alongside three existing squares—the largest existing square and two others.

The three smallest squares have sides of length 1.

What is the side-length of the 12th square?

23 **9.**

> "My car uses just 8 litres per 100 km ", boasted Jim.
> "Mine does 540 km on a full 45 litre tank", said Kim.
> "Mine does 13 km per litre", said Lim.

When the cars are placed in order, with the most economical car first and the least economical last, what is the order?

24 **10.** Part of a wall is to be decorated with a row of four square tiles of three different colours.

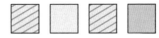

Three different colours of tiles are available and there are at least two tiles of each colour available.

In how many different ways can the row of four tiles be chosen?

24 **11.** The year 2010 belongs to a special sequence of twenty-five consecutive years: each number from 1988 to 2012 contains a repeated digit.

Each of the five years in the box below belongs to a sequence of consecutive years, where each number in the sequence contains at least one repeated digit.

> 2099   2120   2199   2989   3299

Which of them belongs to the next such sequence of at least twenty years?

24 **12.** The list

> 2   1   3   2   2   3   1   4

describes itself, since there are two 1s, three 2s, two 3s and one 4.

There is exactly one other list of eight numbers containing only the numbers 1, 2, 3, and 4 that, in the same way, describes the numbers of 1s, 2s, 3s and 4s in that order.

What is the total number of 1s and 3s in this other list?

24 **13.** Jack dances clockwise around the maypole, making one revolution every five seconds.

Starting from a point diametrically opposite Jack's starting point, Jill dances anticlockwise, making one revolution every six seconds.

How many times do they pass each other in the first minute?

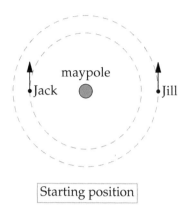

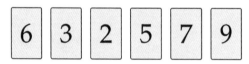

24 **14.** To celebrate the year 2001, a square pavement was made using equal-sized square tiles, coloured either red or blue. In the pattern all the tiles are red apart from those along the two main diagonals, which were made using a total of 2001 blue tiles.

How many red tiles were used?

24 **15.** The six cards shown display the number 632 579.

$$\boxed{6}\ \boxed{3}\ \boxed{2}\ \boxed{5}\ \boxed{7}\ \boxed{9}$$

Each 'turn' exchanges the positions of two *adjacent* cards. For example, after one turn the cards could show 632 759.

Starting from the original 632 579, what is the least number of turns required so that the cards display a number which is divisible by 4?

25 **16.** For Beatrix's latest art installation, she has fixed a 2×2 square sheet of steel to a wall.

She has two 1×2 magnetic tiles, both of which she attaches to the steel sheet, in any orientation, so that none of the sheet is visible and the line separating the two tiles cannot be seen. As shown alongside, one tile has one grey cell and one hatched cell; the other tile has one grey cell and one spotted cell.

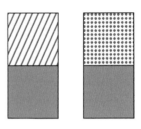

How many different looking 2×2 installations can Beatrix obtain?

25 **17.** A square is divided into adjacent pairs of smaller squares with sides of integer length, as shown in the diagram.

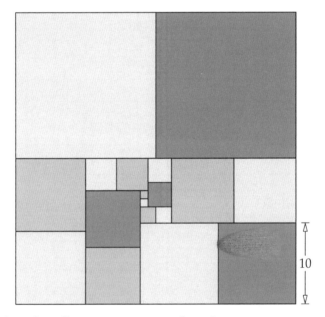

Each size of smaller square occurs only twice.

One square has sides of length 10, as shown.

What is the area of the whole square?

25 **18.** Sixty 20p coins are placed side by side in a row.

Every second 20p coin is then replaced by a 10p coin. Then every third coin in the resulting row is replaced by a 5p coin. Finally every fourth coin in the row is replaced by a 2p coin.

What is the final value of the row?

Part III

Remarks and answers

What is best in mathematics deserves
not merely to be learnt as a task, but to
be assimilated as a part of daily thought,
and brought again and again before the
mind with ever-renewed encouragement.

Bertrand Russell
The Study of Mathematics

The remarks are intended to help you to arrive at the answer, possibly
using a different approach to any you may have in mind.
An answer is given for every problem in the book.

Exercise 1

1. ☞ *Multiply and divide before adding and subtracting.*
   For example, $6 + 5 - 4$ is equal to 7.

   ANSWER: $6 + 5 - 4$

2. $1 + 2 - 3 + 4$ is equal to $3 - 3 + 4$.

   ANSWER: $1 - 2 + 3 + 4$

3. The expression is equal to $9 \times (111 - 11 + 1) \div 9$.

   ANSWER: 101

4. Subtracting the smallest amount from 1 gives the largest answer.

   ANSWER: $1 - 0.00001$

5. ☞ *Multiply and divide before adding and subtracting.*
   The expression is equal to $0 + 1$.

   ANSWER: 1

6. The expression is equal to $2010 + 0 + 0$.

   ANSWER: 2010

7. ANSWER: 699.3

8. ☞ *Multiply and divide before adding and subtracting.*
   The expression is equal to $0.3 + 0.12$.

   ANSWER: 0.42

9. ANSWER: 3996

10. The expression is equal to $900 + 9$.

    ANSWER: 909

11. The expression is equal to half of $(200 - 1)$.

Answer: $99\tfrac{1}{2}$

12. The expression is equal to $1001 \times 2 \times 5$.

Answer: 10010

13. The expression is equal to half of $(1000 - 1)$.

Answer: $499\tfrac{1}{2}$

14. The number of *gaps* between the lamp-posts is $4 - 1$.

Answer: $75\,\text{m}$

15. Answer: 59979

16. Answer: 0.505

17. ☞ *Multiply and divide before adding and subtracting.*
For example, the statement $3 + 5 \times 4 = 23$ is *true*.

Answer: $3 + 6 \times 4 = 36$

18. Divide $5000\,\text{m}$ by $400\,\text{m}$.

Answer: $12\tfrac{1}{2}$

19. ☞ *Multiply and divide before adding and subtracting.*
For example, the expression $1 \times 8 + 8 \times 1$ is equal to $8 + 8$.

Answer: $3 \times 9 + 9 \times 3 = 36$

20. He *saves* 9×7 minutes.

Answer: 63

Exercise 2

1. ☞ *Multiply and divide before adding and subtracting.*

   ☞ *A positive integer is a multiple of 5 when the rightmost digit is either 0 or 5, and not otherwise.*

   ANSWER: $1 + 2 \times 3 \times 4$

2. ☞ *A multiple of 10 is also a multiple of 5.*

   $2\,400\,040\,002$ is equal to $10 \times 240\,004\,000 + 2$.

   ANSWER: 2

3. ☞ *A positive integer is a multiple of 3 when the sum of its digits is a multiple of 3, and not otherwise.*

   Consider the three-digit integer with leftmost digit $d - 1$, middle digit d and rightmost digit $d + 1$. For any digit d from 2 to 8, the sum of the digits of this integer is equal to $3d$. For example, the sum of the digits of 567 is equal to 3×6.

   ANSWER: Five

4. ANSWER: 112

5. $354\,972$ is equal to $35 \times 10000 + 49 \times 100 + 7 \times 10 + 2$.

   ANSWER: 2

6. ☞ *A positive integer is a multiple of 5 when the rightmost digit is either 0 or 5, and not otherwise.*

   ☞ *A positive integer is a multiple of 6 when it is both even and a multiple of 3, and not otherwise.*

   ANSWER: 27

7. $7\,000\,010$ is equal to $7 \times 1\,000\,000 + 7 + 3$.

   ANSWER: 3

8. Note that $111\,111 = 111 \times 1001$ and that $1001 = 7 \times 11 \times 13$.

   ANSWER: $111\,111$

9. ANSWER: eighteen

10. ☞ *A positive integer is a multiple of 5 when the rightmost digit is either 0 or 5, and not otherwise.*

ANSWER: One

11. ☞ *A positive integer is a multiple of 3 when the sum of its digits is a multiple of 3, and not otherwise.*

ANSWER: 567 890

12. ANSWER: 7

13. ☞ *When divided by 9, a positive integer and the sum of its digits have the same remainder.*

ANSWER: 861

14. ☞ *A positive integer is even when the rightmost digit is even, and not otherwise.*

☞ *A positive integer is a multiple of 3 when the sum of its digits is a multiple of 3, and not otherwise.*

☞ *A positive integer is a multiple of 4 when the two-digit integer formed by the two rightmost digits is a multiple of 4, and not otherwise.*

☞ *A positive integer is a multiple of 5 when the rightmost digit is either 0 or 5, and not otherwise.*

☞ *A positive integer is a multiple of 6 when it is both even and a multiple of 3, and not otherwise.*

ANSWER: 1234 is a multiple of 4

Exercise 3

1. ANSWER: 2.34

2. Any point where three arcs meet has to be either the first or the last point drawn.

   ANSWER:

3. In the last clock face, the sum of numbers eaten is equal to $1 + 2 + 3 + 4 + 5$.

   ANSWER:

4. There are 17 matchsticks in the diagram, but only 3×4 matchsticks are needed for three small squares that touch only at corners.

   ANSWER: Five

5. From the wording of the question, it is safe to assume that there *are* some children in the family!

   Each child has at least one sister, so there are some female children. Any female child has at least one sister, so there are at least two girls in the family.

   ANSWER: Four

6. In the pie chart, the two grey regions have equal area, but are smaller than the white region.

   ANSWER:

7. The empty small rectangle in the second row down should contain 58, because $105 - 47 = 58$.

ANSWER: Ɛ

8. The point $(0, 1)$ is 1 unit from the origin along the y-axis.

ANSWER: (I'I)

9. The diagram alongside shows that it is possible to turn the formation upside down by moving two plates.

It is clearly not possible to turn the formation upside down by moving just one plate.

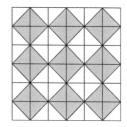

ANSWER: OML

10. Divide the large square into 36 small squares, as shown in the diagram alongside. Exactly one half of each of these small squares is shaded.

ANSWER: $\dfrac{1}{2}$

11. The second empty block on the bottom row should display 8, because $15 - 7 = 8$.

ANSWER: II

12. Jo is the oldest child, because all the arrows at J lead away from J.

ANSWER: Ko, Co, Mo, Uo, Jo

13. The diagram alongside shows the rail and the part of the field that the guinea-pig can reach.

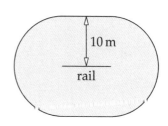

ANSWER:

14. The number of notes was $659\,500 - 659\,384 + 1$.

ANSWER: £585

15. The rulers overlap by $4\,\text{cm} + 3\,\text{cm}$.

ANSWER: 13

16. The diameter of each circle is $5\,\text{cm}$.

ANSWER: 4 cm

17. The middle diagram shows two pieces of string; each of the other diagrams is possible and shows a single piece of string.

ANSWER: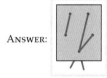

18. ☛ *Multiply and divide before adding and subtracting.*

I owe £55 × 55 and have £50 × 50 + £5 × 5 in my piggy bank.

ANSWER: No, I have £500 too little.

19. The person at position P can see exactly two other people.

ANSWER: Caz

20. One quarter of the members are girls.

ANSWER: 3 : 1

Exercise 4

1. ☞ *There are 60 minutes in an hour.*

   The match lasted 95 minutes.

   ANSWER: 4:05 pm

2. ☞ *There are 60 minutes in an hour.*

   There are 2 hours less 22 minutes until midnight.

   ANSWER: 98

3. ☞ *There are 60 minutes in an hour.*
   ☞ *There are 24 hours in a day.*

   There are 60 × 24 minutes in a day.

   ANSWER: 120

4. ☞ *There are 60 minutes in an hour.*

   The train left at 17:45.

   ANSWER: 18:27

5. ANSWER: 358

6. 1998 was 87 years after 1911.

   ANSWER: 149

7. When Gollum *does* eat fish on a Monday, he *does not* on the following Monday; when he *does not* eat fish on a Monday, he *does* on the following Monday.

   ANSWER: once a fortnight

8. ANSWER: 72

9. ANSWER: 155

10. ANSWER: 162

11. ☞ *There are 60 minutes in an hour.*

A Supertape rewinds in $6 \times 60 \div 18$ minutes.

ANSWER: 20

12. ☞ *There are 60 minutes in an hour.*

The train left at 17:46.

ANSWER: 18:29

13. ☞ *There are 60 minutes in an hour.*

From 11:11 until 23:23 on the same day there are 12 hours and 12 minutes.

ANSWER: 732

14. ☞ *There are 60 minutes in an hour.*

Adding 12 hours converts am to pm; $45 + 44$ minutes is equal to 1 hour 29 minutes.

ANSWER: 7:29 pm

15. ☞ *There are 365 days in a year (366 days in a leap year).*

☞ *There are 12 months in a year.*

☞ *There are 7 days in a week.*

☞ *There are 24 hours in a day.*

One year is equal to at most 366 days, so 125 days is longer than $\frac{1}{3}$ of a year.

ANSWER: 3002 hours

16. ☞ *There are 365 days in a year (366 days in a leap year).*

☞ *There are 24 hours in a day.*

☞ *There are 60 minutes in an hour.*

The number of minutes in a year is at most $60 \times 24 \times 366$, which is equal to $558\,720$.

ANSWER: a year

17. ☞ *There are 60 seconds in a minute.*

Halving 16 minutes six times gives 15 seconds.

ANSWER: Tuesday

18. In every minute the octopus opens 8 jars.

ANSWER: 480

19. ☞ *There are 365 days in a year (366 days in a leap year).*

The number of days since the bridge opened is roughly 365 × 44, which is about 1500.

ANSWER: 20 000

Exercise 5

1. Answer: 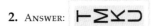 One

2. Answer: ⊢ ⋝ ⋋ ⊃

3. The faces with 1 pip, 4 pips and 5 pips have four lines of symmetry each.

   Answer: Three

4. The given pattern does not have a line of symmetry, whereas the pattern in the diagram alongside has.

   Answer: One

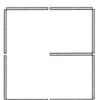

5. The diagram alongside shows the clock after it is reflected in a vertical mirror.

   Answer: half past one

6. A reflected letter J, for example, will never look the same as the original, no matter how it is rotated.

   Answer: Three

7. Before it is reflected, the clock at 1:30 pm looks like the diagram alongside.

   Answer:

8. The diagram alongside shows the lines of symmetry added to the design.

ANSWER: Four.

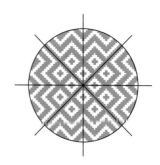

9. ANSWER: **TMKU**

10. The squares marked with a dot need to be visited more than once, but it is possible to go through the maze visiting every other square exactly once.

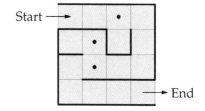

ANSWER: Three.

11. Each time Beatrix folds the paper, the number of holes is doubled.

ANSWER: Sixteen.

12. One of the shapes does not unfold to give half a square.

ANSWER:

13. The diagram shows the original rod (top) and the rod after performing the first two rotations (bottom).

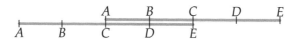

ANSWER: D

14. Each 'arm' of the L-shape needs to be cut.
One way of arranging the 3 × 3 square is shown in the diagram alongside.

Answer: Three

15. The diagram alongside shows how to place the mirror so that the part of the square on one side of the mirror and its reflection forms an octagon.

Answer: E

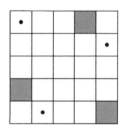

16. The pieces may be reassembled either by matching *PX* with *XR*, or by matching *QR* with *PS* or with *SX*.

Answer: Three

17. In order for the figure to have rotational symmetry of order 2, it is necessary to shade the three cells indicated by a dot in the diagram alongside. But then the resulting figure already has at least one line of symmetry.

Answer: Three

Exercise 6

1. ☞ *1 cm is equal to 10 mm.*

There are 100 teeth and 99 gaps.

ANSWER: 19.9 cm

2. ☞ *1 litre is equal to 1000 ml.*

200 ml is equal to one fifth of a litre.

ANSWER: a cupful

3. ☞ *1 m is equal to 1000 mm.*

2010 mm is just over 2 m.

ANSWER: a table

4. ☞ *1 kg is equal to 1000 g.*

100 £1 coins have mass of 1 kg.

ANSWER: £100 000

5. ☞ *1 tonne is equal to 1000 kg.*

There are 400 bags in one tonne.

ANSWER: £2500

6. ☞ *1 km is approximately equal to 5 ÷ 8 miles.*

1.2 km is approximately 1.2 × 5 ÷ 8 miles.

ANSWER: 0.75 miles

7. 1 barrel is equal to 9 bushels, which are equal to 4 × 9 pecks.

ANSWER: 35

8. Four arms are equal to 2 × 4 = 8 forearms, which are equal to 2 × 8 hands, ...

ANSWER: 64

9. ☞ *1 kg is equal to 1000 g.*

$1000 \times 500\,000$ seeds weigh 1 kg.

Answer: 500

10. One crotchet is equal to $2 \times 2 \times 2$ demisemiquavers.

Answer: 32

11. ☞ *1 kg is equal to 1000 g.*

Together, all their answer sheets weighed $140\,000 \times 6$ g.

Answer: 840

12. ☞ *1 kg is equal to 1000 g.*

The total weight of raspberries that I picked was 31×300 g.

Answer: 9.3 kg

13. ☞ *1 litre is equal to 1000 ml.*

After I completed the first coat, there were 1500 millilitres left.

Answer: 500

14. ☞ *1 m is equal to 1000 mm.*
☞ *1 km is equal to 1000 m.*

One million is equal to 1000×1000.

Answer: 1 km

15. ☞ *1 m is equal to 1000 mm.*
☞ *There are 365 days in a year (366 days in a leap year).*

In 1000 years there are roughly 1000×365 days.

Answer: 0.003

Exercise 7

1. Answer: 823

2. ☞ *The number b as a percentage of the number c is equal to* $\dfrac{b}{c} \times 100$.

Answer: 5

3. For example, $\frac{1}{6}$ of 84 means $\frac{1}{6} \times 84$, which is equal to 14.

Answer: $\frac{1}{4}$ of 60

4. ☞ *1% is equal to one hundredth.*
50% of £60 is equal to £30.

Answer: £12

5. $\dfrac{1}{25}$ is equal to 0.04.

Answer: 0.29

6. The difference between $\dfrac{1}{3}$ and $\dfrac{1}{4}$ is $\dfrac{1}{12}$.

Answer: 36

7. She shared two thirds of the bar amongst her children; four twelfths is equal to one third.

Answer: Eight

8. ☞ *Dividing by* $\dfrac{1}{b}$ *is the same as multiplying by b.*

$6 \div \dfrac{1}{2}$ is equal to 12.

Answer: $4 \div \dfrac{1}{4}$

9. ☞ *For positive numbers, when b is greater than c then $\frac{1}{b}$ is less than $\frac{1}{c}$.*

$\frac{1}{5}$ is less than $\frac{1}{4}$.

ANSWER: $\frac{9}{\text{I}}$

10. ☞ *For positive numbers, when b is greater than c then $\frac{a}{b}$ is less than $\frac{a}{c}$.*

$\frac{12}{23}$ is equal to $1 - \frac{11}{23}$.

The value closest to 1 is obtained by subtracting the smallest amount from 1.

ANSWER: $\frac{\angle 9}{9\varsigma}$

11. $2 + 4 + 6 + 8 + 10 + 12 + 14 + 16 + 18 + 20$ is twice $1 + 2 + 3 + 4 + 5 + 6 + 7 + 8 + 9 + 10$.

ANSWER: ζ

12. When the tankard is one quarter empty it is three quarters full.

ANSWER: ʃɯ09I

13. ☞ *For positive numbers, when b is greater than c then $\frac{1}{b}$ is less than $\frac{1}{c}$.*

$\frac{1}{n} - \frac{1}{n+1} = \frac{1}{n \times (n+1)}$.

ANSWER: $\frac{\angle}{\text{I}} - \frac{9}{\text{I}}$

14. ☞ *Dividing by $\frac{1}{b}$ is the same as multiplying by b.*

$1 - \frac{3}{4}$ is equal to $\frac{1}{4}$.

ANSWER: 9I

15. ☞ *Dividing by* $\frac{1}{b}$ *is the same as multiplying by b.*

ANSWER: $\frac{1}{2} \div \frac{1}{4}$

16. 120 tonnes was two thirds of the cargo, so that 60 tonnes was lost.

ANSWER: 180

17. Only one of the five fractions is smaller than $\frac{1}{2}$.

ANSWER: $\frac{6}{13}$

18. ☞ *The number b as a percentage of the number c is equal to* $\frac{b}{c} \times 100$.

The increase in Gill's weight was $50\,\text{kg} - 5\,\text{kg}$.

ANSWER: 900

19. The number of boys travelling by bus is equal to half of 52% of the pupils.

ANSWER: 38

20. Ross drinks two-fifths of the mineral water and Rachel drinks three-fifths.

ANSWER: 450 ml

Exercise 8

1. Answer: ⅼ203

2. The next year that has the units digit equal to twice the thousands digit is 2014.

   Answer: 0ⅼ

3. The smallest 4-digit integer is 1000.

   Answer: ⅼ

4. The next time all the digits are different the meter reading will be 098 671.

   Answer: ⅼ4

5. The product has at least two factors equal to 5, and at least two factors equal to 2.

   Answer: 0

6. The table shows the value of the seventh number for the different choices of the six equal single-digit positive integers.

Six equal numbers	Seventh number
1	11
2	5
3 or above	negative

   Answer: 5

7. Apart from the rightmost two, all the digits of two numbers with the smallest possible difference are the same.

   Answer: 6

8. As a decimal, $\dfrac{20}{11}$ is equal to 1.818....

   Answer: two

9. When the digit 4 is replaced by the digit 3, the number 99 949 is reduced by 100.

ANSWER: 45 678

10. The digits in the year may be either 1, 1 and any number of zeros, or 2 and any number of zeros. So the years are 11, 101, 110, ..., and 2, 20, ...

ANSWER: Nine

11. There is only one possibility for each of P, Q, R, S and T, as shown in the diagram alongside.

$$\begin{array}{r} 7\ 6\ 2\ 1\ 8 \\ -\ 5\ 3\ 9\ 9\ 6 \\ \hline 2\ 2\ 2\ 2\ 2 \end{array}$$

ANSWER: 29

12. The number of the year has the form '2*dd*2' for some digit *d*.

ANSWER: None

Exercise 9

1. Seats T18 to T38 are between us.

ANSWER: ɪ̄Z

2. $9 \times 987\,654\,321$ is equal to $8\ldots89$.

ANSWER: əu!N

3. ☞ *First work out anything in brackets.*

$(1 + 2) \times (3 + 4)$ is equal to 3×7.

ANSWER: $(Ᵽ \times Ɛ) \times (Z + \mathrm{I})$

4. ☞ *Multiply and divide before adding and subtracting.*

$1 + 9 + 9 \times 7$ is equal to $1 + 9 + 63$.

ANSWER: $Ɫ + 6 \times 6 + \mathrm{I}$

5. The largest number is 7.

ANSWER: $Ɫ$

6. ☞ *First work out anything in brackets.*

The expression is equal to $(0 - 1) - (1 - 0)$.

ANSWER: $Z-$

7. ANSWER: Ϛɪɪ ZƐⱣϚ

8. The smallest number of the most expensive item is offered for £20.

ANSWER: ʇəllnɔ quɐl ɐ

9. The rightmost two digits in $123\,456\,789 \times 8$ are 12.

ANSWER: Ɛ

10. ANSWER: $880Z-$

11. A medium cartridge can print 900 pages.

ANSWER: 0ϚƐ1

12. The largest number is 0.9.

ANSWER: 0.73

13. For example, 195 is equal to 201 − 6.

ANSWER: Four

14. For example, 22 − 2 × 3 is equal to ?? − 6.

ANSWER: 4 + 4 × 2

15. ☞ *Multiply and divide before adding and subtracting.*

ANSWER: 25

16. ☞ *When b is positive, $\sqrt{a \times b^2}$ is equal to $\sqrt{a} \times b$.*
☞ *Written as a decimal, $\sqrt{2}$ is equal to 1.414 21 . . . .*
$\sqrt{18}$ is equal to $\sqrt{2} \times 3$.

ANSWER: 4.2

17. $123 − 45 − 67 + 89 = 100$.

ANSWER: −1

18. ☞ *Multiply and divide before adding and subtracting.*

$4 \times 5 + 67 = 20 + 67$ and $45 + 6 \times 7 = 45 + 42$, so that the first statement is correct.

ANSWER: $9 \times 6 + 67 = 67 + 7 \times 3$

19. Each number after the second is twice the previous number.

ANSWER: 640

20. The number is around $(8 \times 60 \div 70)$ million.

ANSWER: 7 000 000

Exercise 10

1. The total cost of the postcards and stamps was $10 \times 10 + 19 \times 10$ pence, and $10x + 19x = 29x$.

ANSWER: £2.70

2. $2n + 3n + 5n = 10n$.

ANSWER: 170

3. Let the number of girls be g, so that the number of boys is $600 - g$. But $600 - g = g - 30$.

ANSWER: 315

4. $1 + a + b + a \times b = (1 + a) \times (1 + b)$.

ANSWER: 1999

5. Let the number of balls that Andy collects be $2b$, so that Roger collects b balls and Maria collects $2b - 5$. But $2b + b + (2b - 5) = 35$.

ANSWER: 16

6. Let the amount of chocolate that Reg has be c, so that Peg has $6c$ and Meg has $2c$.

ANSWER: Three

7. Let the number of boys in the family be b, so that Peter has $b - 1$ brothers. Hence he has $3 \times (b - 1)$ sisters, which is equal to the number of girls in the family.
But Louise has $2 \times b$ sisters, so that the number of girls in the family is equal to $1 + 2 \times b$.

ANSWER: 13

8. Let the weight of Lisa's bucket be w kg and the weight of half a bucket of water be h kg. Then we have

$$w + 2h = 21$$
$$\text{and} \quad w + h = 12.$$

ANSWER: 3 kg

9. The second equation is superfluous.

ANSWER: $\square + \square$

10. Let the weight of luggage that is carried free be w kg. Then Laa-laa is charged for 50 kg $- w$ kg, so that $50 - w = 15$.

ANSWER: 40

11. Let the weight of the fish be $3w$ kg. Then $3w = 2 + w$.

ANSWER: Three

12. From the first equation, one ■ is equal to two ▲s, and from the second, one ● is equal to three ▲s.

ANSWER: Six

13. Let the height from which it was originally dropped be h cm. Then after the first bounce it rises to a height $\frac{1}{3}h$ cm.

ANSWER: 81 cm

14. Let Dilly be d years old now. Then her age in 4 years time will be $d + 4$ years, and Dally will be $d + 11$ years old.

ANSWER: 13

Exercise 11

1. 10 additional unit cells are lit to make the 'o' bold.

ANSWER: 24

2. There are 8 triangles with one vertex at the centre of the rectangle.

ANSWER: 12

3. ☞ *Suppose there are m ways of making one choice and, whichever first choice is made, n ways of making a second choice, then there are m × n ways of making both choices in succession* [multiplication principle].

There are two ways of getting from *P* to the middle, and two ways of getting from the middle to *Q*.

ANSWER: Four

4. A bottle that is half full is also half empty!

ANSWER: 10

5. The number of regions in the diagram is equal to twice the number of circles: each of the smallest circles is divided into two regions; each of the other circles contributes an extra two regions.

ANSWER: 32

6. Nine houses are knocked down.

ANSWER: 114

7. Each koala has six thumbs.

ANSWER: 60

8. There are 4 × 3 ways to choose two of the four small triangles, when the choice *A* followed by *B* is counted as different to *B* followed by *A*; otherwise there are 4 × 3 ÷ 2 ways.

ANSWER: Six

9. All totals from 1 + 1 to 4 + 5 are possible.

ANSWER: Eight

10. I make seven sandwiches.

Answer: 28

11. Consider two faces that have an edge in common, and paint them in different colours, shown as grey and white in the diagram alongside. Then there is a third face (hatched in the diagram) that has an edge in common with each of these two, so that a third colour is required.

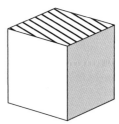

The whole cube may be painted using just three colours by now painting opposite faces with the same colour.

Answer: Three

12. Carol may get either Holly's card or Ivy's card.

Answer: Two

13. This problem is essentially the same as question 11 above.

Answer: Three

14. There are four hexagons congruent to that hatched on the left below, and two congruent to that on the right.

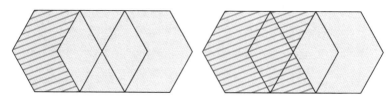

Answer: 12

15. ☛ *Suppose there are m ways of making one choice and, whichever first choice is made, n ways of making a second choice, then there are m × n ways of making both choices in succession* [multiplication principle].

When both outside pages started as end 'panels', they are not from the same side of the sheet. There are only two ways to achieve this.

When one of the two middle panels ends up on the outside, the other outside page is one of the two adjacent panels on the same side of the sheet. There are 2×2 ways to achieve this.

ANSWER: Six

16. ☛ *Suppose there are m ways of making one choice and, whichever first choice is made, n ways of making a second choice, then there are m × n ways of making both choices in succession* [multiplication principle].

There are three different routes from S to U.

ANSWER: 18

17. The three digits are either 9, 8, 8 in some order, or 9, 9, 7 in some order. In each case, the digit that is not repeated may be in one of three positions in the three-digit number.

ANSWER: Six

18. ☛ *Suppose there are m ways of making one choice and, whichever first choice is made, n ways of making a second choice, then there are m × n ways of making both choices in succession* [multiplication principle].

There are eight ways to choose the first person in a bout, and six ways to choose the second. So there are 8×6 ways to choose who wrestles in a bout. But this counts each bout twice: 'A wrestling B' is counted in addition to 'B wrestling A'.

ANSWER: 24

19. Taking 12 jellybeans fails since their flavours may be, for example, 8 watermelon and 4 vanilla.

But *any* selection of 13 jellybeans necessarily includes one of each flavour.

ANSWER: 13

Exercise 12

1. ☞ *The base angles of an isosceles triangle are equal.*

   ☞ *An exterior angle of a triangle is equal to the sum of the interior opposite angles.*

   $130 = x + 90$.

   ANSWER: 40

2. ☞ *An exterior angle of a triangle is equal to the sum of the interior opposite angles.*

   ANSWER: 28

3. ☞ *Angles at a point add up to 360°.*

   ☞ *An exterior angle of a triangle is equal to the sum of the interior opposite angles.*

   $100 = x + 36$.

   ANSWER: 64

4. ☞ *Each interior angle of a square is equal to 90°.*

   ☞ *Each interior angle of an equilateral triangle is equal to 60°.*

   ☞ *An exterior angle of a triangle is equal to the sum of the interior opposite angles.*

   The exterior angle *MJK* of triangle *JMC* is equal to 90°.

   ANSWER: 30°

5. ☞ *Angles on a straight line add up to 180°.*

   ☞ *An exterior angle of a triangle is equal to the sum of the interior opposite angles.*

   $120 = x + 70$.

   ANSWER: 50

6. ☞ *The angles in a triangle add up to 180°.*

   The diagram shows two overlapping triangles.

   ANSWER: 360°

7. ☞ *An exterior angle of a triangle is equal to the sum of the interior opposite angles.*

Divide the quadrilateral into two triangles, as shown in the diagram alongside.

$y = a + 15$ and $z = b + 25$.

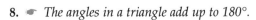

ANSWER: 75

8. ☞ *The angles in a triangle add up to 180°.*

$\frac{1}{2}(y + z) = x$ and $x + y + z = 180$.

ANSWER: 60

9. ☞ *Corresponding angles on parallel lines are equal.*

☞ *Angles on a straight line add up to 180°.*

☞ *An exterior angle of a triangle is equal to the sum of the interior opposite angles.*

$134 = x + 48$.

ANSWER: 86

10. ☞ *Each interior angle of a square is equal to 90°.*

☞ *Each interior angle of an equilateral triangle is equal to 60°.*

☞ *Angles at a point add up to 360°.*

☞ *The base angles of an isosceles triangle are equal.*

☞ *The angles in a triangle add up to 180°.*

$2x + 120 = 180$.

ANSWER: 30

11. ☞ *Each interior angle of a square is equal to 90°.*

☞ *Each interior angle of an equilateral triangle is equal to 60°.*

☞ *Angles at a point add up to 360°.*

ANSWER: 120

12. ☞ *Corresponding angles on parallel lines are equal.*

   ☞ *Each interior angle of an equilateral triangle is equal to 60°.*

As shown in the diagram alongside, add a line through a vertex of the triangle parallel to two sides of the rectangle.

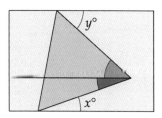

Answer: 09

13. ☞ *Angles on a straight line add up to 180°.*

   ☞ *An exterior angle of a triangle is equal to the sum of the interior opposite angles.*

$113 = x + 71.$

Answer: 42

14. ☞ *The base angles of an isosceles triangle are equal.*

   ☞ *Each interior angle of a square is equal to 90°.*

   ☞ *An exterior angle of a triangle is equal to the sum of the interior opposite angles.*

As shown in the diagram alongside, add a third equal square.

We deduce that $x - 90 + 90 = 70 + 70.$

Answer: 140

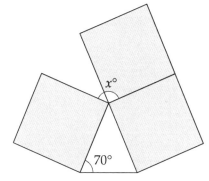

15. ☞ *The angles in a triangle add up to 180°.*

Let the angle at Q be $2q°$, and the angle at R be $2r°$, so that $2q + 2r + 40 = 180$. Then $q° + r° + $ angle $RSQ = 180°.$

Answer: 110°

16. ☞ *An exterior angle of a triangle is equal to the sum of the interior opposite angles.*

   ☞ *Angles on a straight line add up to 180°.*

   Angle *MRP* is equal to 50°.

   ANSWER: 130°

17. ☞ *The base angles of an isosceles triangle are equal.*

   ☞ *The angles of a triangle add up to 180°.*

   ANSWER: 30°

18. See the diagram on the left below, which shows the bottom left-hand corner.

   At any corner of the envelope the two flaps overlap. Hence $x + y$ is greater than 90, so that $x + 90 + y$ is greater than 180.

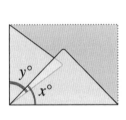 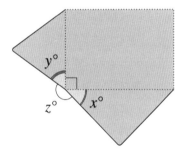

   Therefore when the flaps are unfolded, as in the diagram on the right above, the angle $z°$ is less than 180°.

   ANSWER: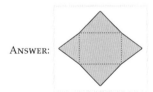

Exercise 13

1. The rectangles labelled S and U are orange and yellow, in some order.

ANSWER: The rectangle labelled S.

2. ANSWER: b

3. Each bottle essentially costs $1, but you cannot spend the final $2.

ANSWER: Eight

4. There are eight children altogether. Each child buys seven eggs.

ANSWER: 56

5. From the left, the order is either Amy, Ben, Chris, or Amy, Chris, Ben.

ANSWER: Amy is furthest to the left.

6. Every morning, Dilly has essentially learnt three words.
(When she wakes on the next morning, Dilly will have forgotten two of the fourteen words.)

ANSWER: Friday

7. The number of students in either the band or the orchestra (or both) is $60 + 20 - 12$.

ANSWER: 32

8. The sentence already contains eight copies of the letter e.

ANSWER: Two

9. The first two in a successful sequence of four moves is shown in the diagrams below, where the glasses that have been turned over on each move are shown dotted.

Assign 0 to a glass with its base at the bottom, and 1 to a glass with its base at the top. Then the total for the starting position is 0, and the total for the end position is 4. But a move changes the total from even to odd, or vice versa, so that the number of moves is even, and two moves clearly fail.

ANSWER: Four

Exercise 14

1. Answer: 1.75 m

2. ☛ *Distance is equal to speed × time.*

Gill walked between 3 × 5 and 4 × 5 kilometres.

Answer: 19 km

3. He rowed 25 048 miles in about 13 years.

Answer: 2000

4. ☛ *The sum of n numbers is equal to n × (their average).*

Before the new member joined, the total age was 4 × 19.

Answer: 20

5. Usain's mum has run 50 m and Turbo has run one fifth of that.

Answer: 40 m

6. ☛ *The sum of n numbers is equal to n × (their average).*

The total number of spots of members of the squad is 6 × 12.

Answer: Four

7. The two fractions are 6 ninths and 4 ninths.

Answer: $\frac{5}{6}$

8. ☛ *The average of an even number of consecutive integers is equal to the average of the middle two.*

The average of the ten integers is $\frac{1}{2}$.

Answer: 5

9. ☛ *The sum of n numbers is equal to n × (their average).*

The total of Karen's marks was 2 × 78.

Answer: 84

10. The team has 5 × 12 toes in total, and there are 12 team members.

Answer: Five

Exercise 15

1. The perimeter of the square has four sides; two-fifths of two of them are black.

   ANSWER: $\frac{1}{5}$

2. ☞ *The area of a triangle is equal to $\frac{1}{2} \times$ base $\times$ height.*

   The triangle has base 3 cm and height 3 cm.

   ANSWER: 4.5

3. Annabel walks 4×8 cm.

   ANSWER: 8 cm

4. Suppose that each side of the square has length 3, so that the length of the perimeter of the square is 12.

   ANSWER: 3 : 5

5. Removing A, B or D decreases the length of the perimeter by 2, and removing C increases the length of the perimeter by 2.

   ANSWER: E

6. The length of the perimeter of the shape is equal to that of a rectangle measuring 6 cm × 2 cm.

   ANSWER: 16 cm

7. ☞ *The area of a triangle is equal to $\frac{1}{2} \times$ base $\times$ height.*

   The ratio of the heights of the triangles is equal to 2 : 3.

   ANSWER: $\frac{1}{3}$

8. Divide the large square into eight congruent rectangles, as shown in the diagram alongside. Four of these rectangles have one half shaded grey.

ANSWER: $\frac{1}{4}$

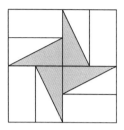

9. The diagram alongside shows the two arrows drawn on the same grid.

ANSWER: $6\,\text{cm}^2$

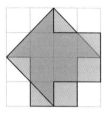

10. The area of the 'hole' is equal to $16\,\text{cm}^2$.

ANSWER: 26

11. The diagram alongside shows the region occupied by the pen over four successive days.

ANSWER: $15\,\text{m}^2$

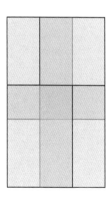

12. Four $1\,\text{cm} \times 1\,\text{cm}$ squares are covered twice.

ANSWER: $36\,\text{cm}^2$

13. ☞ *The diagonals of a rectangle bisect one another.*
   ☞ *Triangles with equal bases and the same height have equal areas.*

ANSWER: $1:1$

14. ☞ *The sum of the lengths of two sides of a triangle is greater than the length of the third side.*

The length of the equal sides may be anything between 9 cm and 6 cm (inclusive).

ANSWER: Four

15. ☞ *1 m is equal to 1000 mm.*

0.2 millimetres is equal to $0.2 \div 1000$ metres.

ANSWER: 5000

16. $130 \times x - 50 \times x = 80 \times x.$

ANSWER: 8000

17. The sides of the square have length 50 cm.

ANSWER: $100 \, cm^2$

18. The region outside the overlap consists of two rectangles; one of these measures $6 \, cm \times 1 \, cm$.

ANSWER: $27 \, cm^2$

Exercise 16

1. ☞ *A positive integer with exactly three factors is equal to the square of a prime.*

   ANSWER: 25

2. Let the numbers of 20p and 26p stamps be m and n respectively. Then $m \times 20 + n \times 26 = 101$, so that $13n = 101 - 10m$. Therefore $101 - 10m$ is a positive multiple of 13, and the only possibility is 91.

   ANSWER: One

3. Each van can carry at most two crates.

   ANSWER: 12

4. ☞ *The number 1 is not prime.*

   ☞ *A positive integer is a multiple of 3 when its digits add up to a multiple of 3, and not otherwise.*

   ☞ *A positive integer is a multiple of 5 when the rightmost digit is either 0 or 5, and not otherwise.*

   Three of the numbers in the list are even.

   ANSWER: None

5. 1998 is equal to $2 \times 3 \times 111$.

   ANSWER: 42

6. Let each child eat c beans. Then the number of beans that Pa Bean eats is equal to $23 - 4c$. Thus $23 - 4c$ is greater than $2c$, but at most half of 23.

   ANSWER: 11

7. There is only one way to get a total of £1.25 with one coin of each denomination used.

   ANSWER: 5p

8. The primes are 2, 3, 5, 7, 11, 13, ... When one of the numbers is 2, the sum is even, and so not prime; $3 + 5 + 7$ is not prime.

ANSWER: 6I

9. The primes are 2, 3, 5, 7, 11, 13, ...

ANSWER: 00I

10. Let the numbers of rectangular and round tables needed be m and n respectively. Then $8 \times m + 5 \times n = 36$.

ANSWER: ˣⁱS

11. ☞ *Suppose there are m ways of making one choice and, whichever first choice is made, n ways of making a second choice, then there are m × n ways of making both choices in succession* [multiplication principle].

A label $q + r$ is a multiple of 3 precisely when:
  (i) either both q and r are multiples of 3;
  (ii) or q and r have remainders 1 and 2 (in either order) on dividing by 3.

The remainders on dividing each of the eight numbers in the diagram by 3 are shown in the following table.

Number	Remainder
1, 4, 7	1
2, 5, 8	2
3, 6	0

Hence the number of labels that are multiples of 3 is $3 \times 3 + 1$.

ANSWER: 0I

12. From the given entries, we deduce that the input factors are as shown in the diagram alongside.

×	3	5	8	10	6
2	P	10		20	
5	15	Q	40		
6	18		R	60	
4		20		S	24
7			56		T

ANSWER: 161

13. ☞ *The remainder on dividing the product $q \times r$ of two positive integers by a prime p is equal to q times the remainder on dividing r by p (possibly minus a multiple of p).*

The number of nuggets left for Snow White is equal to the remainder on dividing the original number of nuggets by 7.

The remainder on dividing 100 by 7 is 2.

ANSWER: 300

14. ☞ *A positive integer is a multiple of 3 when its digits add up to a multiple of 3, and not otherwise.*

☞ *A positive integer is a multiple of 5 when the rightmost digit is either 0 or 5, and not otherwise.*

All the even years can be discounted. 2009 is divisible by 7.

ANSWER: 2011

15. The prime digits are 2, 3, 5 and 7.

ANSWER: Four

16. ☞ *A positive integer is a multiple of the positive integers q and r when it is a multiple of the lowest common multiple of q and r, and not otherwise.*

The lowest common multiple of all of the integers from 1 to 10 inclusive is equal to $2^3 \times 3^2 \times 5 \times 7$.

ANSWER: 45 × 56

17. ☞ *Suppose there are m ways of making one choice and, whichever first choice is made, n ways of making a second choice, then there are m × n ways of making both choices in succession* [multiplication principle].

There are $3 \times 2 \times 1$ possible products to check.

ANSWER: 105

18. ☞ *A positive integer is a multiple of 3 when its digits add up to a multiple of 3, and not otherwise.*

$1 + 3 + 5 = 9.$

ANSWER: None

Exercise 17

1. The total number of pips on the top and bottom faces is equal to $2 \times 7 - 5$.

   ANSWER: 6

2. Any point where three lines meet has to be either the first or the last point drawn.

   ANSWER: only at R or S

3. Third place receives one sixth of the prize money.

   ANSWER: $\dfrac{1}{12}$

4. Two touching coins can never be removed.

   ANSWER: Three

5. The calculation written normally is $927 - 54$.

   ANSWER: 378

6. After the digits are replaced, the subtractions are

   $$75 - 64 \qquad 85 - 74 \qquad 95 - 84 \qquad 05 - 94 \qquad 15 - 04$$

   ANSWER: $50 - 49$

7. The third term is 3; after that, every term is double the previous one.

   ANSWER: 72

8. The sequence is $-3, 0, 2, -1, 1, 2, 2, 5, \ldots$.

   ANSWER: the 13th term

9. The top bar is used when 0, 2, 3, 5, 6, 7, 8 and 9 are shown.

   ANSWER: [image]

10. The schematic diagram shows the relative positions of the signs.

Answer: 393 miles

11. ☞ *The mode of a list of numbers is the number that occurs most frequently in the list.*

Answer: the 94° sector

12. Twelve goals were scored in the whole match, so the winning goal margin was an even number.

Answer: Jokers won by three goals

13. In the diagram, parts of the line drawn earlier appear *below* parts drawn later. The part between A and B (not passing through any other labelled point) is at the bottom.

Answer: B

14. The diagram below shows the positions of the points.

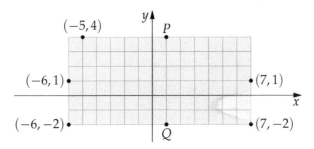

Answer: $(-6, -2)$

15. $100 = 4 + 6 \times 16$.

Answer: ◇ and △

16. To reverse the process, subtract 2, reverse the digits and halve the result.

Answer: 45

17. The sum of consecutive cubes starting from 1^3 is *always* a square.

As demonstrated by the diagram below, the sum of the first n cubes is equal to the square of the sum of the first n positive integers, for any positive integer n.

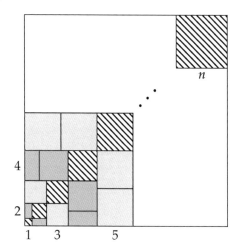

Answer: Four

18. The diagram alongside shows the path of the snail.

Answer: (6, 5)

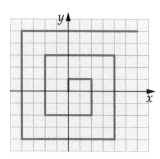

19. The length of the perimeter of Tom's patch is 12 m, which is equal to the length of 60 worms.

Answer: 81½

20. There are twelve cubes of each colour. The rows of seven and five cubes are the same colour, which can only be yellow.

Answer: pɚɹ

Exercise 18

1. When the net is folded, A, B, C and E end up adjacent to X.

ANSWER: D

2. The letters U, K, M and P are adjacent to O.

ANSWER: W

3. When the net is folded to form the cube, the edges A and B fold together, as do the two unlabelled edges between A and X.

ANSWER: E

4. The pyramid had eight edges before the corners were cut off. Three new edges are created by cutting each of the bottom corners off.

ANSWER: 24

5. The sculpture may be considered as being made up from six 2 × 1 × 1 blocks.

ANSWER: 12

6. Together the three visible faces make up half the surface area of the cuboid. Their combined area is $2\frac{1}{4}$ times the area of one of the visible unhatched faces.

ANSWER: 16

7. The blue faces of the small cubes form the faces of the original wooden cube.

   The unpainted faces of the small cubes form both sides of slices through the original wooden cube, such as that shown in the diagram alongside.

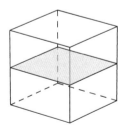

ANSWER: $\frac{1}{2}$

8. The first net does form a cube, as shown by the diagram alongside, where the dark lines correspond to the boundary of the net.

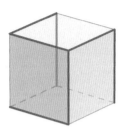

ANSWER: Five

9. The largest cube he can cut measures 2 inches × 2 inches × 2 inches, and three of these have a volume of 3 × 8 cubic inches.

ANSWER: 15

10. From above, the pyramid looks like a square with sides of length 4 m.

ANSWER: 72 m²

11. From above, the solid looks like a cross made from five 5 cm × 5 cm squares.

ANSWER: 750

12. Each dimension of the cuboid is an integer number of centimetres, their product is equal to 72 cm³, and two of them (other than the height) add up to 8 cm.

ANSWER: 6 cm

13. For the cube in the diagram alongside, the orientation of the letter H relative to the aeroplane is not correct.

ANSWER:

14. There are 12 cubes that have at least one grey face.

ANSWER: 15

15. By considering each layer of the final solid, we see that 20 + 8 + 12 + 8 + 20 small cubes remain.

ANSWER: 89

16. The diagram alongside shows the blue 'cross'. Next, each edge of the hidden central cube has an edge of a yellow cube attached. Then a face of a yellow cube is attached to each of the six uncovered faces.

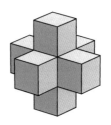

ANSWER: 81

17. The opened out cube contains two lines of three squares joined by a single edge, shown dotted in the diagram alongside.

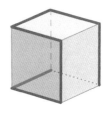

ANSWER:

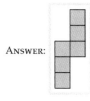

Exercise 19

1. $\dfrac{4}{7}$ is greater than $\dfrac{5}{9}$ because 4×9 is greater than 5×7.

   ANSWER: $\dfrac{4}{7}$

2. ☛ *For positive numbers, when b is greater than c then $\dfrac{1}{b}$ is less than $\dfrac{1}{c}$.*

   Two of the fractions are less than 1; the other three are equal to $1 + \dfrac{1}{5}$, $1 + \dfrac{1}{4}$ and $1 + \dfrac{1}{6}$.

   ANSWER: $\dfrac{1+4}{1+3}$

3. ☛ *1% is equal to one hundredth.*

   15% of the rest is 15% of 90%, which is equal to $\dfrac{15}{100} \times 90\%$.

   ANSWER: 76.5

4. 30 tulips are yellow and 10 are red.

   ANSWER: $\dfrac{1}{4}$

5. 6957 is less than 7000, so that 4×6957 is less than $28\,000$.

   ANSWER: $\dfrac{6957}{31248}$

6. She has three-quarters of two-thirds of the original amount left.

   ANSWER: $\dfrac{1}{2}$

7. $\frac{3}{5}$ is equal to 0.6.

   ANSWER: $\frac{3}{5}, 0.5, \frac{4}{5}, 0.9$

8. ☞ *1% is equal to one hundredth.*

1% of the final total is equal to $108 \div 18$.

ANSWER: 009

9. ☞ *1% is equal to one hundredth.*

80% of 80% of the volume of water is equal to 1152 ml.

ANSWER: 1800 ml

10. There are 9 boys in the class.

ANSWER: 5 : 3

11. The values of p and q follow from the given entries; the value of r can now be found.

ANSWER: $\dfrac{6}{16}$

12. The numerator of the second fraction is twice the numerator of the first fraction.

ANSWER: $\dfrac{1}{7}$

13. The denominator of the fraction is twice the numerator.

ANSWER: 6779

14. The second and third boxes contain four-ninths of the pears. Hence one-third of the number of pears is twelve.

ANSWER: 16

15. The ratio of junior members to senior members to veterans is equal to $15 : 10 : 4$.

ANSWER: 58

16. $\dfrac{1}{12} = \dfrac{2}{24}$.

ANSWER: 8

17. $\frac{1}{2}$ is equal to $\frac{6}{12}$, and $\frac{3}{4}$ is equal to $\frac{9}{12}$.

ANSWER: $\frac{2}{3}$

18. ☞ *1% is equal to one hundredth.*

The three points Range Hill scored in the second half are 10% of the points in the match.

ANSWER: $\frac{1}{5}$

19. The ratio of boys to girls to adults is equal to 15 : 20 : 28.

ANSWER: $5 : 4$

20. ☞ *1% is equal to one hundredth.*

So far I have succeeded in 245 out of 500 games.

Let the number of extra games I need to play be g. After playing them, I will have succeeded in $245 + g$ out of $500 + g$ games.

ANSWER: 10

Exercise 20

1. ANSWER:

2. When the robot is facing due east it has turned through a total angle of 90°, or 450°, or ....

ANSWER: 45 m

3. The number of words is equal to $256 \times 33 \times 9$.

ANSWER: 75 000

4. Throwing 6 and −3 achieves 3.

ANSWER: 7

5. Whichever routes are chosen, Jo has to go more than once to the stations shown grey in the diagram below.

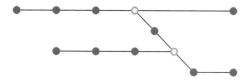

ANSWER: Three

6. The tiling may be produced by repeating a polygon with six sides. Each copy of the polygon consists of one grey tile and one hatched tile (see the diagram below).

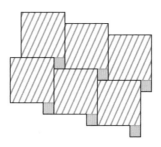

ANSWER: 1 : 1

7. The number of 'off' switches may be 3, 2, 1 or 0.

ANSWER: 13

8. ☞ *Suppose there are m ways of making one choice and, whichever first choice is made, n ways of making a second choice, then there are m × n ways of making both choices in succession* [multiplication principle].

To obtain a triangle, choose one point from P, Q and R and two from S, T and U, or vice versa. Four of these triangles are not right-angled.

ANSWER: 14

9. The units digit of $44^2 + 77^2$ is equal to the units digit of $6 + 9$.

ANSWER: $88^2 + 33^2 = 8833$

10. The number of 5p coins may be 2, 1 or 0.

ANSWER: 11

11. 5^6 is equal to $25 \times 25 \times 25$.

ANSWER: $15\,618 = 1 + 5^6 - 1 \times 8$

12. The strip of paper has only one side.

ANSWER: X, Y and Z

13. One way to achieve the largest number of dots is to add the circle shown in the diagram alongside.

ANSWER: Eight

14. The positive cubes are 1, 8, 27, 64, 125, ...

ANSWER: 216

15. Two roads are used each time a village is visited.

ANSWER: Three

16. ☞ *1 m is equal to 100 cm.*

After he has told nine lies, Pinocchio's nose is $2^9 \times 5$ cm long.

ANSWER: a tennis court

17. The newspaper has nine sheets of four pages, starting with a sheet with pages 1, 2, 35 and 36.

ANSWER: 9, 27, 28

18. The two numbers in the empty boxes on the bottom row add up to 90, so the two numbers in the empty boxes on the next row up add up to $12 + 90 + 78$.

ANSWER: 360

19. There are at least two possibilities: in one A has 2 and 9; in the other A has 4 and 7.

ANSWER: It is not possible to tell.

Exercise 21

1. Only 4 and 5 can be adjacent to 2; only 1 and 2 can be adjacent to 4.

Answer: 5

2. It follows from the diagonal '1-2-*M*' that *M* = 3.

Answer: 4

3. In the second column, only the top cell can be a cross.

Answer: A

4. The numbers 2, 3, 4, 5, 6, 7 and 8 add up to 35.

Answer: 7

5. The integers from 7 to 15 inclusive add up to 99, so that the total of each row, column, or main diagonal is 33.

Answer: 8

6. The integers from 1 to 9 inclusive add up to 45.

Answer: 8

7. Each letter appears exactly once in every row, column and main diagonal.

Answer: D

8. Let the digit in the top circle be *d*. Then the total of the three lines of four circles is equal to $(45 + 2 + 5 + d) \div 3$.

Answer: 20

9. The total of the first column is equal to $x + 18$, so that the central cell is $x - 2$. Now the unkown cells in the right-hand column may be found in terms of x.

Answer: 12

Exercise 22

1. Their current ages add up to 56.

Answer: 2024

2. ☞ *1 hour is equal to 60 minutes.*

The two times were actually 12:51 and 15.01.

Answer: 2 hours 10 minutes

3. ☞ *1 hour is equal to 60 minutes.*

The fifth set lasted 481 minutes and the match lasted 665 minutes.

Answer: $\frac{3}{4}$

4. ☞ *1 week is equal to 7 days.*

In nine days Peri travels 9 m, then has a rest day, so it takes 99 days to cover 90 m.

Answer: Tuesday

5. ☞ *1 week is equal to 7 days.*

☞ *1 year is equal to 12 months.*

50 days is 7 weeks and 1 day; 50 months is 4 years and 2 months.

Answer: 56

6. ☞ *1 hour is equal to 60 minutes.*

Every hour the two watches are 3 minutes further apart.

Answer: 8 am on Monday

7. ☞ *1 week is equal to 7 days.*

Only 6 days out of 7 have been included in Granny's age.

Answer: 86

8. The first digit of the hour only changes as the hour moves from 09 to 10, from 19 to 20 and from 23 to 00.

ANSWER: Three

9. When the hour hand turns through one twelfth of a revolution, the minute hand turns through one revolution. Therefore *relative to the hour hand* the minute hand turns through eleven revolutions in a period of twelve hours.

ANSWER: 22

10. ☞ *1 hour is equal to 60 minutes.*

In 2 hours they had gone from $\dfrac{4}{12}$ to $\dfrac{9}{12}$ of the way up.

ANSWER: 12:24 pm

11. ☞ *1 minute is equal to 60 seconds.*

☞ *1 hour is equal to 60 minutes.*

The time taken to answer n questions is equal to $2^n - 1$ seconds, and in 1 hour there are 60×60 seconds.

ANSWER: 55

Exercise 23

1. ☞ *Each interior angle of an equilateral triangle is equal to 60°.*

   ☞ *An exterior angle of a triangle is equal to the sum of the interior opposite angles.*

   ☞ *Each interior angle of a square is equal to 90°.*

   ☞ *Angles on a straight line add up to 180°.*

   Considering the angles at the bottom corner of the square, we get $(x + 60) + (y + 60) = 90 + 180$.

   ANSWER: 150

2. ☞ *Angles at a point add up to 360°.*

   ☞ *The angles in a triangle add up to 180°.*

   There are five points and two triangles in the diagram.

   ANSWER: 1440°

3. ☞ *Angles on a straight line add up to 180°.*

   ☞ *An exterior angle of a triangle is equal to the sum of the interior opposite angles.*

   ANSWER: 104

4. ☞ *Each interior angle of an equilateral triangle is equal to 60°.*

   ☞ *An exterior angle of a triangle is equal to the sum of the interior opposite angles.*

   Angle QTP is equal to $35° + 60°$.

   ANSWER: 135

5. ☞ *The angles in a triangle add up to 180°.*

   ☞ *Sides opposite equal angles of a triangle are equal.*

   $(x + 10) + (2x - 40) + (3x - 90) = 180$, so that $x = 50$.

   ANSWER: equilateral

6. ☞ *The angles in a triangle add up to 180°.*

☞ *Each interior angle of a rectangle is equal to 90°.*

ANSWER: 75°

7. ☞ *Angles on a straight line add up to 180°.*

☞ *The base angles of an isosceles triangle are equal.*

☞ *An exterior angle of a triangle is equal to the sum of the interior opposite angles.*

ANSWER: 27°

8. ☞ *The base angles of an isosceles triangle are equal.*

☞ *An exterior angle of a triangle is equal to the sum of the interior opposite angles.*

ANSWER: 35

9. ☞ *Each exterior angle of a regular pentagon is equal to 72°.*

☞ *The base angles of an isosceles triangle are equal.*

☞ *An exterior angle of a triangle is equal to the sum of the interior opposite angles.*

☞ *Each interior angle of a regular pentagon is equal to 108°.*

☞ *Each interior angle of a regular hexagon is equal to 120°.*

Angle QRP is equal to 36°.

ANSWER: 48°

10. ☞ *The base angles of an isosceles triangle are equal.*

☞ *An exterior angle of a triangle is equal to the sum of the interior opposite angles.*

ANSWER: $h - x$

11. ☞ *The base angles of an isosceles triangle are equal.*

☞ *An exterior angle of a triangle is equal to the sum of the interior opposite angles.*

☞ *The angles in a triangle add up to 180°.*

Let angles QSU and TSR be equal to $x°$ and $y°$ respectively. Then angle QRP is equal to $(x° + 40°) - y°$.

ANSWER: $100°$

12. ☞ *The base angles of an isosceles triangle are equal.*

☞ *An exterior angle of a triangle is equal to the sum of the interior opposite angles.*

$p = r + (r - q)$

ANSWER: $\frac{1}{2}(p + q)$

13. ☞ *Vertically opposite angles are equal.*

☞ *The base angles of an isosceles triangle are equal.*

☞ *Angles on a straight line add up to 180°.*

☞ *An exterior angle of a triangle is equal to the sum of the interior opposite angles.*

ANSWER: Three

14. ☞ *An exterior angle of a triangle is equal to the sum of the interior opposite angles.*

☞ *The base angles of an isosceles triangle are equal.*

The same angle at V is exterior to both triangle VWU and triangle VYZ, so that $y + z = (x + z) + (x + z)$.

ANSWER: $x = \frac{y - z}{2}$

15. ☞ *The angles in a triangle add up to 180°.*

$8m + 13n = 130$, so that m is a multiple of 13.

ANSWER: 15

Exercise 24

1. Let the value of a ping be p, and the value of a pong be q. Then $5p + 5q = 2q + 11p$.

   ANSWER: Two

2. Let b boys join the group. Then $(18 + b) : 30 = 5 : 3$.

   ANSWER: 32

3. We have the equations

$$x + 2y = 5y - x$$
$$\text{and} \quad x + 2y = 3x - y.$$

   ANSWER: $(10, 6)$

4. The area is equal to $4 \times (2a + 6)$.

   ANSWER: $8(a + 3)$

5. Let my weight be m kg, the baby's weight be b kg, and the nurse's weight be n kg. Then

$$m + b = 78,$$
$$n + b = 69$$
$$\text{and} \quad m + n = 137.$$

   Adding up the three equations, we get $2m + 2n + 2b = 284$.

   ANSWER: 142 kg

6. Let my age now be a years, so that Granny is $4a$ years old. Then $4a - 5 = 5 \times (a - 5)$.

   ANSWER: 100

7. $\dfrac{(a \times b) \times (b \times c)}{c \times a}$ is equal to b^2.

   ANSWER: $10\frac{1}{2}$

8. Let a and b be the missing numbers in the second and third cells from the left; then we have

$$2a = b + 8$$
$$\text{and} \quad 2b = a + 20.$$

ANSWER: 24

9. Let the number of sides of the polygon be n; then this is also the number of vertices. Joining each vertex to one of $n - 3$ others forms a diagonal.

ANSWER: Seven

10. Half the perimeter length of the quadrilateral is 13.

ANSWER: 36

11. Four of each type of fruit cost $154 + 170$ pence.

ANSWER: 81p

12. The second row and third column give simultaneous equations for ♥ and ✈.

ANSWER: 3

13. Let the number of bricks that each has sold be b. Then Bob gets $£6 \times \dfrac{b}{10}$ and Geri gets $£7 \times \dfrac{b}{12}$.

ANSWER: 240

14. Let each block measure $\ell\,\text{cm} \times h\,\text{cm}$. Then the height of the table is equal to $96\,\text{cm} + h\,\text{cm} - \ell\,\text{cm}$ and is also equal to $84\,\text{cm} + \ell\,\text{cm} - h\,\text{cm}$.

ANSWER: 90 cm

15. By adding the two pieces of information, we find that eleven green notes and eleven blue notes are worth 77 zogs.

ANSWER: 19

16. $2 \times$ (the length of the longer side of each rectangle) $- x = y$.

ANSWER: $\dfrac{z}{h + x}$

17. Three times the sum of Amrita's four numbers is equal to $115 + 153 + 169 + 181$.

ANSWER: 16

18. Let the width of each rectangle be $2x$ cm; then the height of each rectangle is equal to $3x$ cm.

ANSWER: 270 cm²

19. Let the first term be a and the second term be b. Then $2a + 3b = 2004$.

ANSWER: 666

Exercise 25

1. The first statement cannot be true, because then the second statement would also be true, contradicting the fact that only one of the five statements is true.

ANSWER: The fifth statement is true.

2. Pages normally read by BCG BCG... are now read by CG CG CG....

ANSWER: Six

3. Either the fare is paid exactly (which is not possible in fewer than four coins) or the driver gives change (which transaction is not possible in fewer than three coins).

ANSWER: Three

4. Either the Knave of Clubs is lying, or he is telling the truth.

ANSWER: Two

5. Jill lost four games, so won three.

ANSWER: Seven

6. The total number of chocolates is $p + q$, so that when each box has $\frac{1}{2}(p + q)$ chocolates then they have an equal number.

ANSWER: $\frac{1}{2}(p - q) + 1$

7. The statements contradict one another, so no more than one of them is true.

ANSWER: One

8. The integer 5 has to be in a 5×1 rectangle, which can only fit across the top.

The integer 4 is in either a 4×1 or a 2×2 rectangle; but a 4×1 rectangle fails.

ANSWER: 4

9. Three of the dominoes have to be placed together, as shown in the diagram alongside. The remaining three also have to be placed together, but 'either way round' relative to the first group.

   ANSWER: ᴼᴹ⊥

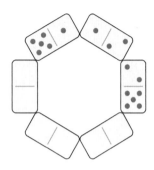

10. The list is 3, 4, *, *, 3, *, 4, ...

    ANSWER: ⊥

11. The number of sides is equal to the number of corners, which is no more than the number of dots.

    The diagram alongside shows part of a polygon that uses all the dots.

    ANSWER: 9⊥

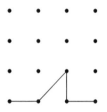

12. If Dilly brings green gloves only, then she needs to bring five, because any number less than that might all be right-hand gloves.

    ANSWER: ɹnoℲ

13. The sequence of trips CC, C, A, C gets one adult (only) across the river and returns the boat to the original side.

    ANSWER: ǝuᴎ

14. Boris runs up 99 steps, Spike runs up 78 steps, and Percival runs up 61 steps. Boris would run up 100 steps in the same time that Spike would run up 80 steps, and in that time Percival would run up 60 steps.

    ANSWER: dᴚS

15. The distance between Q and R may be found from the distances between Q, V, S, P, U and R.

    ANSWER: ⛌⊥

Exercise 26

1. The hexagon may be dissected into congruent equilateral triangles, as shown in the diagram alongside.

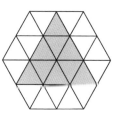

ANSWER: $\frac{3}{8}$

2. Each cut is longer than 1 cm. The length of the perimeter of A is equal to 3 cm plus 6 cuts.

ANSWER: E

3. The length of the perimeter of the whole shape is the same as the length of the perimeter of a 1002 cm × 1003 cm rectangle.

ANSWER: 4010

4. ☛ *The area of a triangle is equal to $\frac{1}{2}$ × base × height.*

ANSWER: $3\,cm^2$

5. ☛ *The area of a circle with radius r is equal to $\pi \times r^2$.*

The shape comprises three semicircles with one semicircle removed.

ANSWER: $5\pi\,cm^2$

6. The length of the perimeter of the 'L' shape is equal to four times the length of the longer side of each rectangle.

ANSWER: 10 cm

7. ☛ *The area of a triangle is equal to $\frac{1}{2}$ × base × height.*

The unshaded area comprises two triangles.

ANSWER: $\frac{11}{16}$

8. The side-length of each square is $a \div 4$. The length of wire required is equal to four times the length of the rectangle plus five times its height.

Answer: $\dfrac{31a}{4}$

9. ☞ *The area of a triangle is equal to $\frac{1}{2} \times base \times height$.*

The area of the pentagon is $3\frac{1}{2} \times 9$ small squares.

Answer: $\dfrac{7}{2}$

10. Adding one hexagon increases the length of the perimeter by 4 cm.

Answer: 502

11. In the parallelogram with longest perimeter, three pairs of sides of the triangles will be placed together.

Answer: 76 cm

12. The hexagon may be dissected into congruent equilateral triangles, and half-equilateral triangles, as shown in the diagram alongside.

Answer: $\dfrac{1}{2}$

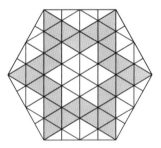

13. The hexagon may be dissected into congruent equilateral triangles, as shown in the diagram alongside.

Answer: $\dfrac{2}{9}$

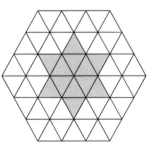

14. The area of the region where squares overlap is equal to $(1 + 4 + 9 + 16 + 1.5)\,\text{cm}^2 - 5\,\text{cm} \times 5.5\,\text{cm}$.

ANSWER: $4\,\text{cm}^2$

15. Divide the central square into four congruent triangles, as shown in the diagram alongside. Then the given grey region comprises two rectangles and three such triangles.

ANSWER: $\dfrac{1}{4}$

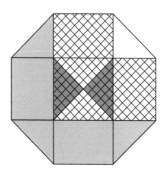

16. The total area of the three squares is equal to $117\,\text{cm}^2$ plus twice the area of the overlap.

ANSWER: $7\,\text{cm}$

17. The sum of the four perimeter lengths given in the diagram is equal to the perimeter length of the hatched parallelogram added to the perimeter length of $WXYZ$.

ANSWER: $7\,\text{cm}$

18. The total area shaded grey is equal to $(11\,\text{cm})^2 + (7\,\text{cm})^2$ minus the area of the overlap.

ANSWER: $64\,\text{cm}^2$

Exercise 27

1. The winning candidate receives at least $83 \div 4$ votes, but they cannot have received 21 votes because, in that case, the others may have received 21, 21 and 20 votes.

   ANSWER: 22

2. An odd number of 5-bar boxes are needed because 12 is even and 2005 is odd. But neither one nor three 5-bar boxes work.

   ANSWER: 170

3. The special offer rate is 10p each, so I can buy at most 20 lollipops. However, I can buy no more than 18 at the special rate.

   ANSWER: 19

4. Sam's age in years changed from a square to a prime when it changed from 1 to 2; no other odd square works, because adding 1 gives an even number greater than 2, which is not prime.

   ANSWER: Four

5. They will all eat together again for the first time after a number of days that is equal to the lowest common multiple of 1, 2, 3, 4, 5 and 6.

   ANSWER: 60

6. The only even prime number is 2.

   ANSWER: Four

7. The sum of the positive integers is 49.

   ANSWER: 28

8. Since the sum is even, one of the three numbers is 2.

   ANSWER: 24

9. Let the number of adult tickets sold be a. Then the number of children's tickets sold is equal to $1320 - a \times 3$, and $a + (1320 - a \times 3)$ is less than 600.

   ANSWER: 361

10. Let the number of stamps bought by Evariste be e, and the number bought by Sophie be s. Then $11e + 7s = 100$, so that $11e - 2$ is a (positive) multiple of 7 less than 98; only one value of e works.

ANSWER: 12

11. None of the numbers is 2. There are only seven odd prime numbers less than 20.

ANSWER: 24

12. ☞ *A positive integer is a multiple of 3 when its digits add up to a multiple of 3, and not otherwise.*

When d is equal to 2, 5 or 8, then the sum of the digits of the three-digit across number is a multiple of 3.
$143 = 11 \times 13$; $517 = 11 \times 47$.

ANSWER: 7

13. The number is 1 less than a multiple of 3, 4 and 5.

ANSWER: 3

14. N is at least 3 and divides 24.

ANSWER: 57

15. Let the number of points gained for a win be w, and for a draw be d. Then $7w + 3d = 44$, so that $7w - 2$ is a multiple of 3 less than 42.

ANSWER: 31

16. ☞ *A positive integer is a multiple of 3 when its digits add up to a multiple of 3, and not otherwise.*

   ☞ *A positive integer is a multiple of 5 when the rightmost digit is either 0 or 5, and not otherwise.*

The rightmost digit cannot be 0, 1, 2, 4, 5, 6, 7 or 8. Also $203 = 7 \times 29$, and $209 = 11 \times 19$.

ANSWER: None

17. ☞ *When m and n are positive integers, an integer that is a multiple of m × n is also a multiple of m.*

3, 5, 7 and 15 are also factors.

ANSWER: ⅄0⊺

18. ☞ *When m and n are positive integers, an integer that is a multiple of m × n is also a multiple of m.*

☞ *A positive integer is a multiple of 5 when the rightmost digit is either 0 or 5, and not otherwise.*

☞ *A positive integer is a multiple of 9 when its digits add up to a multiple of 9, and not otherwise.*

The largest five-digit palindromic number that is a multiple of 45 is 59 895.

ANSWER: 0606

19. 113 is prime. $119 = 7 \times 17$ may be placed next to $112 = 7 \times 16$.

ANSWER: oʍ⊥

20. Let the number of girls in Miss Quaffley's class be g, and the number of boys be b. Then $12b + 17g + 3(b + g) = 305$, so that $3b + 4g = 61$; also, $b + g$ is a multiple of 3. Therefore $g + 2$ is a multiple of 9. But g cannot be more than 15.

ANSWER: uǝʌǝS

Exercise 28

1. C is equal to 4 and B is equal to 1.

ANSWER: a

2. ☞ *A positive integer is a multiple of 9 when its digits add up to a multiple of 9, and not otherwise.*

$2d + 11$ is a multiple of 9.

ANSWER: 8

3. ☞ *A positive integer is a multiple of 11 when the 'alternating sum' of its digits is a multiple of 11, and not otherwise.*

The alternating sum of '1234d678' is equal to $1 - 2 + 3 - 4 + d - 6 + 7 - 8$.

ANSWER: 6

4. From the 'tens' and 'units' columns, we see that there is a 'carry' from the 'units' column.

ANSWER: $\angle$

5. From the 'units' column, we see that the rightmost digit of $J + M$ is 0. Then from the 'tens' and 'units' columns, we see that $M = C + 1$.

ANSWER: 8I

6. $10 + a - b = 6$ and $c = b - a - 1$.

ANSWER: ε

7. The leftmost digit is never 0, whereas, for any number apart from 1000, any digit that is not the leftmost one may have any value from 0 to 9.

ANSWER: 0

8. ☞ *A positive integer is a multiple of the positive integers q and r when it is a multiple of the lowest common multiple of q and r, and not otherwise.*

   ☞ *A positive integer is a multiple of 3 when its digits add up to a multiple of 3, and not otherwise.*

   The number is a multiple of 20, so that the missing digits are either 00, 20, 40, 60 or 80. But in only one of these options is the number a multiple of three.

   ANSWER: 4

9. The result increases by 100, therefore 952 473 increases by 1800.

   ANSWER: 2 and 4

10. $21 \times 3 = 63; 18 \times 4 = 72$.

    ANSWER: $16 \times 3 = 48$

11. Let the leading school's score after six events be '*ab*', for some digits *a* and *b*. Then $10a + b + 10b + a = 66$, so that $b + a = 6$. Also, '*ab*' is at most $6 \times (5 + 3)$.

    ANSWER: 18

12. The fifth digit is 3, because it is equal to the sum of the first five digits minus the sum of the first four. Similarly, each of the sixth and seventh digits is 3.

    ANSWER: 25

13. M represents 2, and there is more than one 'carry'.

    ANSWER: 42

14. Pages 1 to 9 take nine digits; pages 10 to 99 take 90×2.

    ANSWER: 320

15. Each of the digits is at most 9, so they add up to at most 27. Thus the house number is greater than 402.

    ANSWER: 28

16. The digit 5 cannot appear in the 'units' column, and it is the largest digit. Therefore D is 5.

ANSWER: Ⅎ

17. '$PQPQ$' is equal to 'PQ' × 101, and 'RRR' is equal to R × 111. But $101 \times 111 = 11\,211$.

ANSWER: ƐⅠ

18. $\frac{1}{2}n$ is at least 100, and $2n$ is at most 999.

ANSWER: 00Ɛ

19. Because the first digit in the fourth row is 8, the first digit in the second row is 2. The second digit in the fourth row is 6, and the missing digit in the top row is 3.

ANSWER: ⌞

Exercise 29

1. When the design has rotational symmetry of order 2, every cell apart from the central one will have the same colour as the opposite cell on the other side of the centre.

   When the largest number of cells is black, the central cell will be black.

   ANSWER: Five

2. The diagram alongside shows the poster when it is reflected.

   ANSWER: Four

3. When the paper is unfolded, the hole on the right becomes two non-square rectangles.

   ANSWER: Seven

4. To make the shape in the middle, fold one corner of the paper to meet the opposite corner.

   ANSWER: Three

5. It is impossible in three moves because $7 + 7$ is greater than three times $3 + 1$.

   In four moves the position changes by an even number of cells both left/right and up/down, so that it is also impossible in four moves.

   One successful set of five moves is shown in the diagram alongside.

   ANSWER: Five

   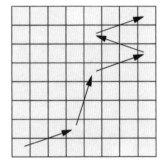

6. Each cut increases the total number of edges by at most four. The diagram alongside shows one way to achieve 12 edges.

   ANSWER: 13

   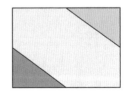

7. Though it is possible to arrange for two adjacent sides of the overlapping region to be at 60°, it is not possible to arrange for three sides to be so.

   The diagram alongside shows one way to achieve a heptagon.

   ANSWER: ǝlɓuɐıɹʇ lɐɹǝʇɐlınbǝ

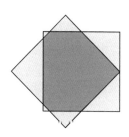

8. The diagram alongside shows how to fit four of the pieces together.

   ANSWER:

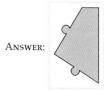

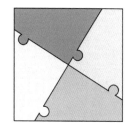

9. The diagram alongside shows the smallest number of moves required to reach each of the positions that is possible in at most three moves.

   ANSWER: ǝʌıℲ

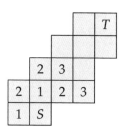

10. The width of each 'step' is equal to 24 cm − 18 cm, and the height is equal to 40 cm − 30 cm.

    ANSWER:

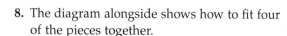

11. ☞ *Each exterior angle of an equilateral triangle is equal to 120°.*

    The circle makes one complete turn as it rolls along each side of the triangle, and one third of a turn at each corner.

    ANSWER: ɹnoℲ

12. The diagram alongside shows the
smallest number of moves required
to reach each of the positions that is
possible in at most two moves.

ANSWER: Three

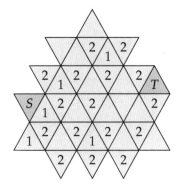

13. In this case, adding a triangle to a
polygon either increases the number
of sides, or decreases the number by
one.

The diagram alongside shows one way
to make a hexagon.

ANSWER: pentagon

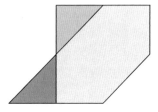

14. The number of uncovered cells cannot be even, because each domino
covers two cells and there are 25 cells in all.

It is impossible for there to be nine cells uncovered when Beatrix stops
(if you find a straightforward way to prove this, please let the author
know).

ANSWER: Seven

15. Rolling the die is equivalent to filling the
grid with pips to make copies of the net of
the die, such as that shown in the diagram
alongside.

ANSWER: One

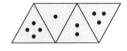

16. Placing three trapezia together in the manner described means that the resulting polygon can have at most eight sides.

The diagram alongside shows one way to make a triangle.

ANSWER: Six

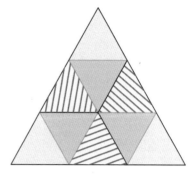

17. A line of symmetry of a polygon passes through one of:
  (i) two vertices;
  (ii) a vertex and the midpoint of one side;
  (iii) the midpoints of two sides.

Let the polygon have n sides; after it is folded in half along a line of symmetry, in these three cases the number of sides of the resulting polygon is equal to:

  (i) $2 + \dfrac{n-2}{2}$;

  (ii) $2 + \dfrac{n-1}{2}$;

  (iii) $2 + \dfrac{n}{2}$.

By setting each of these equal to 3, it follows that the final triangle results from folding a quadrilateral, or a triangle.

ANSWER: Four

Exercise 30

1. The three spaces between the pictures occupy 4800 mm − 4 × 420 mm.

Answer: 730 mm

2. ☞ *Time is equal to distance ÷ speed.*

☞ *There are 60 minutes in an hour.*

Together, the first and third parts of the journey take $\dfrac{56}{96} \times 60$ minutes.

Answer: 09:38

3. ☞ *For any p, q and positive a:* $\quad a^p \div a^q = a^{p-q}$.

☞ *For any p, q and positive a:* $\quad (a^p)^q = a^{pq}$.

8^2 is equal to 2^6.

Answer: 4

4. The sum of the code numbers for the letters in MATHS is $10 + 1 + 16 + 6 + 15$.

Answer: GEOMETRY

5. The current row totals are 36, 34, 32 and 34, so that the two numbers are in the first and third rows.

Answer: 28

6. The diagram alongside shows the number of ways of reaching some of the cells.

Answer: 25

	1	2	4
1	1	2	5
2	2	1	

7. The codes for RECTANGLE and TRIANGLE are related.

Answer: 19 051 200

8. The first four squares have sides of length 1, 1, 1 and 3. After that, the side-length of each square is just the sum of the side-lengths of the previous two.

ANSWER: 123

9. Using 44 litres, Jim's car will go 550 km.

ANSWER: Jim's car Jim's, Kim's

10. ☞ *Suppose there are m ways of making one choice and, whichever first choice is made, n ways of making a second choice, then there are m × n ways of making both choices in succession* [multiplication principle].

There are three ways of choosing the colour that appears twice, and six ways of arranging these two tiles.

ANSWER: 36

11. The longest such sequence containing 2099 is 2099, 2100, 2101, 2102.

ANSWER: 2120

12. Let the list be as shown in the box.

a	1	*b*	2	*c*	3	*d*	4

There are eight numbers in the list, so that $a + b + c + d = 8$. Also, a cannot be equal to 1, and d cannot be greater than 1.

ANSWER: 9

13. ☞ *1 minute is equal to 60 seconds.*

The diagram below indicates their progress in the first 30 seconds.

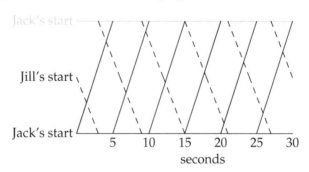

ANSWER: 22

14. There were 1001 tiles along each diagonal.

ANSWER: 1 000 000

15. ☞ *A positive integer is a multiple of 4 when the two-digit integer formed by the two rightmost digits is a multiple of 4, and not otherwise.*

The two rightmost digits need to be odd and even, in that order.

ANSWER: Three

16. ☞ *Suppose there are m ways of making one choice and, whichever first choice is made, n ways of making a second choice, then there are m × n ways of making both choices in succession* [multiplication principle].

There are four ways of choosing which cell of the installation is spotted. Any arrangement of the four cells in the installation may be achieved by placing the two tiles.

ANSWER: 12

17. In increasing order, let the lengths of the sides of the four smallest squares be a, b, c and d. Then $c + a = 2b$ and $d + 2a = 2c$, so that $d = 4b - 4a$. Hence d is a (positive) multiple of 4, and 8 is too big.

ANSWER: 1296

18. (i) A coin in a position that is a multiple of 4 is a 2p coin.

(ii) A coin in a position that is a multiple of 3, but not a multiple of 4, is a 5p coin.

(iii) A coin in a position that is a multiple of 2, but not a multiple of 3 nor of 4, is a 10p coin.

(iv) A coin in any other position is a 20p coin.

The number of 10p coins is equal to $\dfrac{60}{2} - \dfrac{60}{3} - \dfrac{60}{4} + \dfrac{60}{3 \times 4}$.

ANSWER: £6.05

Appendix

Sources of the problems

The problems are taken from the JMC papers for the years 1997–2016. The wording of some problems has been edited, and in every case the multiple-choice options have been removed.

The following tables give the sources of all the problems in the book.

Exercise 1

1.	2016 01
2.	2015 01
3.	2014 01
4.	2013 01
5.	2011 01
6.	2010 01
7.	2009 01
8.	2007 01
9.	2006 01
10.	2005 01
11.	2003 01
12.	2002 01
13.	2000 01
14.	1997 01
15.	2016 02
16.	2012 02
17.	2002 02
18.	2016 03
19.	2009 03
20.	2003 03

Exercise 2

1.	2008 01
2.	1998 01
3.	2011 02
4.	2004 02
5.	2007 03
6.	2007 04
7.	1999 04
8.	2009 05
9.	2004 05
10.	2002 05
11.	1997 07
12.	2015 08
13.	2003 08
14.	2016 11

Exercise 3

1.	1999 01
2.	2008 02
3.	2006 02
4.	2001 02
5.	2006 03
6.	1997 03
7.	2015 04
8.	2009 04
9.	2003 04
10.	2007 05
11.	2006 06
12.	1998 06
13.	2001 07
14.	1998 07
15.	2013 08
16.	2002 08
17.	2000 08
18.	1999 08
19.	2012 09
20.	2000 09

Exercise 4

1.	2001 01
2.	2015 02
3.	2014 02
4.	2007 02
5.	2000 02
6.	1998 02
7.	2005 03
8.	2001 03
9.	2016 04
10.	2012 05
11.	2001 05
12.	1998 05
13.	2009 07
14.	2000 07
15.	2010 09
16.	2016 12
17.	2004 12
18.	2001 13
19.	2010 14

Exercise 5

1.	2004 01
2.	2010 02
3.	2009 02
4.	2005 02
5.	1999 03
6.	2012 04
7.	2005 04
8.	2013 05
9.	2000 05
10.	2005 06
11.	2005 09
12.	2016 10
13.	2004 11
14.	2012 12
15.	1998 12
16.	2008 13
17.	2011 15

Exercise 6

1.	2003 02
2.	1999 02
3.	2010 03
4.	2011 04
5.	2008 05
6.	2016 07
7.	2011 07
8.	2008 07
9.	2005 07
10.	2004 07
11.	2000 10
12.	1997 10
13.	2013 13
14.	2014 14
15.	2008 15

Exercise 7

1.	2015 03
2.	2008 03
3.	2002 03
4.	2001 04
5.	2016 05
6.	2015 05
7.	2011 05
8.	2010 06
9.	2007 06
10.	2004 06
11.	2016 08
12.	2012 08
13.	2008 09
14.	1997 09
15.	2007 10
16.	2008 11
17.	1998 11
18.	2009 12
19.	2000 13
20.	1999 14

Exercise 8

1.	2012	01
2.	2004	03
3.	2014	05
4.	2003	05
5.	2010	07
6.	2002	07
7.	2011	09
8.	2009	09
9.	2001	10
10.	2000	11
11.	2014	12
12.	2002	13

Exercise 9

1.	2014	03
2.	2014	04
3.	2000	04
4.	1997	04
5.	2005	05
6.	2013	06
7.	2002	06
8.	2001	06
9.	2015	07
10.	2014	07
11.	2012	07
12.	2001	08
13.	2016	09
14.	2006	09
15.	2015	10
16.	2003	10
17.	2012	11
18.	2005	12
19.	2003	14
20.	2003	15

Exercise 10

1.	1997	02
2.	1998	03
3.	2016	06
4.	1999	06
5.	2013	07
6.	2005	08
7.	2013	09
8.	2002	09
9.	1998	09
10.	1999	10
11.	2015	12
12.	2011	12
13.	1997	12
14.	2000	15

Exercise 11

1.	2011	03
2.	2006	04
3.	2004	04
4.	1998	04
5.	2010	05
6.	2006	05
7.	1997	05
8.	2007	07
9.	1997	08
10.	1999	09
11.	2008	10
12.	2003	11
13.	1997	11
14.	2013	12
15.	2001	12
16.	1999	12
17.	1998	13
18.	2004	14
19.	2009	15

Exercise 12

1.	2013	03
2.	2000	03
3.	2008	04
4.	2002	04
5.	2015	06
6.	2011	06
7.	2006	07
8.	2010	08
9.	2007	09
10.	2014	10
11.	2009	10
12.	2011	11
13.	2003	12
14.	2005	13
15.	2004	13
16.	1999	13
17.	2016	14
18.	2014	15

Exercise 13

1.	2003	06
2.	1997	06
3.	2003	07
4.	1999	07
5.	2007	08
6.	2005	10
7.	2002	11
8.	2006	12
9.	2002	14

Exercise 14

1.	2013	02
2.	2013	04
3.	2015	09
4.	2003	09
5.	2013	11
6.	2007	12
7.	2011	13
8.	2009	13
9.	2009	14
10.	2001	15

Exercise 15

1.	2014	06
2.	2009	06
3.	2008	06
4.	2011	08
5.	2009	08
6.	2008	08
7.	2014	09
8.	2001	09
9.	2012	10
10.	2010	11
11.	2002	12
12.	2000	12
13.	2014	13
14.	2013	14
15.	2007	14
16.	2006	14
17.	1998	14
18.	2010	15

Exercise 16

1. 2012 03
2. 1999 05
3. 2000 06
4. 2014 08
5. 1998 08
6. 2004 09
7. 2004 10
8. 2015 11
9. 1999 11
10. 2010 12
11. 2015 13
12. 2012 13
13. 2006 13
14. 2003 13
15. 2015 14
16. 2015 15
17. 2007 15
18. 2005 15

Exercise 17

1. 2013 10
2. 2011 10
3. 2010 10
4. 2006 10
5. 2002 10
6. 1998 10
7. 2014 11
8. 2009 11
9. 2007 11
10. 2006 11
11. 2005 11
12. 2001 11
13. 2010 13
14. 2007 13
15. 2012 14
16. 2000 14
17. 2016 15
18. 1999 15
19. 1998 15
20. 1997 15

Exercise 18

1. 2010 04
2. 2012 06
3. 2006 08
4. 2004 08
5. 2008 12
6. 2011 14
7. 2008 14
8. 2001 14
9. 2007 17
10. 2015 20
11. 2011 20
12. 2002 20
13. 1999 20
14. 2014 21
15. 1998 24
16. 2005 25
17. 2003 25

Exercise 19

1. 2005 14
2. 1997 14
3. 2013 15
4. 2012 15
5. 2006 15
6. 2004 15
7. 2002 15
8. 2010 16
9. 2009 16
10. 2012 17
11. 2008 17
12. 2015 18
13. 1999 18
14. 2016 19
15. 2013 19
16. 2001 19
17. 2000 19
18. 2007 20
19. 2006 23
20. 2012 24

Exercise 20

1. 2008 16
2. 2004 16
3. 2000 16
4. 1999 16
5. 2014 17
6. 2009 17
7. 2006 17
8. 2005 17
9. 2004 17
10. 2002 17
11. 2014 18
12. 2003 18
13. 2000 18
14. 2015 19
15. 2010 19
16. 2006 19
17. 1997 19
18. 2009 20
19. 1998 20

Exercise 21

1. 2016 13
2. 1997 13
3. 1998 17
4. 2012 18
5. 2006 18
6. 2001 20
7. 2005 21
8. 2014 23
9. 2000 25

Exercise 22

1. 2013 16
2. 1997 16
3. 2011 17
4. 2011 18
5. 2012 20
6. 2000 21
7. 1999 21
8. 2008 22
9. 1999 22
10. 1997 22
11. 2002 25

Exercise 23

1. 2015 16
2. 2007 16
3. 1997 17
4. 2001 18
5. 1998 18
6. 2012 19
7. 2009 19
8. 2008 19
9. 2004 20
10. 2002 21
11. 2011 23
12. 2005 23
13. 2003 23
14. 2015 25
15. 2012 25

Exercise 24

1.	1998	16
2.	2016	17
3.	2010	17
4.	2003	17
5.	2013	18
6.	2008	18
7.	2004	19
8.	2003	19
9.	2002	19
10.	2016	20
11.	2000	20
12.	2008	21
13.	2003	22
14.	2000	22
15.	2009	23
16.	2007	23
17.	2006	24
18.	2004	24
19.	2004	25

Exercise 25

1.	2014	16
2.	2012	16
3.	2001	16
4.	2015	17
5.	2014	19
6.	2014	20
7.	2005	20
8.	2013	21
9.	2012	21
10.	2007	21
11.	2010	23
12.	2001	23
13.	2011	24
14.	1999	24
15.	1997	25

Exercise 26

1.	2006	16
2.	2013	17
3.	2004	18
4.	1997	18
5.	2007	19
6.	2005	19
7.	1998	19
8.	2003	20
9.	2016	21
10.	2010	21
11.	2016	22
12.	2015	22
13.	2012	22
14.	2015	23
15.	2014	24
16.	2013	24
17.	2009	24
18.	2001	25

Exercise 27

1.	2011	16
2.	2005	16
3.	2001	17
4.	2010	18
5.	2009	18
6.	2011	19
7.	2010	20
8.	2006	20
9.	1997	21
10.	2011	22
11.	2010	22
12.	2007	22
13.	2006	22
14.	2002	22
15.	2013	23
16.	2012	23
17.	2000	23
18.	2015	24
19.	1997	24
20.	2009	25

Exercise 28

1.	2003	16
2.	2000	17
3.	1999	17
4.	2016	18
5.	2007	18
6.	2005	18
7.	2008	20
8.	1997	20
9.	2014	22
10.	2004	22
11.	1998	22
12.	2008	23
13.	2004	23
14.	2007	24
15.	2003	24
16.	2002	24
17.	2010	25
18.	2006	25
19.	1999	25

Exercise 29

1.	2016	16
2.	2002	16
3.	2002	18
4.	1999	19
5.	2013	20
6.	2009	21
7.	2006	21
8.	2004	21
9.	2003	21
10.	2001	22
11.	2002	23
12.	1999	23
13.	1998	23
14.	2016	25
15.	2014	25
16.	2011	25
17.	2007	25

Exercise 30

1.	2015	21
2.	2011	21
3.	2001	21
4.	1998	21
5.	2013	22
6.	2009	22
7.	2005	22
8.	2016	23
9.	1997	23
10.	2016	24
11.	2010	24
12.	2008	24
13.	2005	24
14.	2001	24
15.	2000	24
16.	2013	25
17.	2008	25
18.	1998	25

Index

Only terms from the problems appear in the index. Please also refer to the table of contents.